Bushland Stories

Bushland Stories

AMY ELEANOR MACK

With illustrations by Joyce Dennys

To

The English Three

Mary, Helen, and Margs

CORNSTALK PUBLISHING
an imprint of Angus & Robertson Publishers

Unit 4, Eden Park, 31 Waterloo Road,
North Ryde, NSW, Australia 2113, and
16 Golden Square, London W1R 4BN,
United Kingdom

First published in Australia
by Angus & Robertson Publishers in 1910
Enlarged edition 1914
Other editions 1921, 1923
This selected edition 1983
Reprinted 1987

Copyright text Nancy Phelan and
Sheila Smith-White 1910

National Library of Australia
Cataloguing-in-publication data.

Mack, Amy E. (Amy Eleanor).
  Bushland stories.

  Selections from her Bushland stories.
  Sydney : Angus & Robertson, 1910.
  For children.
  ISBN 0 207 14852 X.

I. Dennys, Joyce. II. Title.

A823'.2

Printed in Singapore

CONTENTS

THE RED GUM'S STORY

THIS is the story the Red Gum told:—

The first thing I can remember about myself is that I was a tiny seed, living with a lot of brothers and sisters in a little wooden cradle. We were all very warm and cosy, and, though we could not see the light, we used to feel the wind as our cradle swayed to and fro on the branch.

Then one day the lid of our cradle seemed to lift up, the wind shook us hard, and out we all tumbled into the air and the sunshine. I do not know what became of my brothers and sisters, for I never saw any of them again, but I was carried along by the wind for a while, and then I dropped to the ground. Of course, I did not know then it was the ground, but I found out the names of all these things later on.

There was a nice soft feeling about the earth which I liked even better than the hard cradle I had been born in, and I snuggled down into it, so that the wind should not carry me any farther. When I had been lying there for a few days, the rain came down, and wet the top of the earth, and as I was afraid of being washed away, I snuggled still deeper into the soil. It was nice gentle rain, and made the earth damp and soft and sweet, and I felt very comfortable, and so I just lay there, and dozed and dreamed.

I do not know quite how long I lay dreaming, but one day I had a curious sensation in my skin, and I felt as if I must rise above the earth and see the sun. This feeling grew worse and worse, until at last the skin that bound me cracked, and I began to grow up through it. I pushed and pushed, and my arm went up higher and higher towards the light, but my feet went deeper still into the earth, and held me firm.

My arm kept on working through the soil, and every day I knew that I was growing nearer to the top, and then, one day, I felt the coolness of the breeze just above me, and in a little while I was through.

Oh, how beautiful the sunlight seemed! I wondered however I could have stayed so long in the dark earth. And yet I was glad that my feet were so firmly rooted in the ground, for that kept me from being blown away. All round me, as far as I could see, was grass, but straight over my head were blue

1

sky and branches. The branches seemed higher than mountains, for you must remember I was not yet as tall as the grass. In fact, I was really only a tiny green point, so small that you never would have noticed me, even if you had been looking for me.

But I was very ambitious, and I did want to see what was on the other side of the grass. So I kept on pushing and pushing, and the good sun warmed me, and I drank in moisture from the air, and food from the earth, and every day I grew stronger and stronger, until in a very short time, instead of being just a green point above the ground, I had spread out into two pretty soft leaves.

I was very proud then, for I was as tall as the grass, and could see on to the other side. And this is what I saw. Beautiful flowers, white, red, and yellow, some not much taller than myself, and some ever so high above my head; and above the flowers was a tree, which made my heart ache with longing when I saw it. It was very, very big—indeed then I thought it must be quite the biggest thing in the world. Its trunk was of a lovely deep red, and it had dozens and dozens of long curving arms, stretching in every direction, and on each branch were beautiful fine leaves, hanging in graceful clusters. Amongst these leaves the birds sang and built their nests, and I thought as I looked at it, "Oh, if only I could grow into a tree like that!"

I did not think that such a tiny thing as I then was could ever be big at all, but I felt that I must get nearer to that beautiful spreading tree. And so every day I kept on trying and trying to reach it, and all the time I was drinking in my food from the earth to make me strong, so that I should have enough strength to carry me up. At length, I found one day that I had shot up through my first two leaves, and had developed two more, quite different from the first. In a little while I grew through these, and then two more leaves came. These also were different from the first two, and never again in my life did I have any more just like the first soft leaves of all.

While I was growing up and up into the air, my feet—or, as I shall now call them, my roots—kept on growing down farther and farther into the ground. As fresh leaves sprouted out, new rootlets also were put forth, which served to hold me fast in the ground, and to drink in food to make me strong.

And so the days and weeks went by, and I grew higher and higher—very slowly it seemed to me, for I was young and impatient, and wanted to grow nearer to the beautiful tree. After a time I noticed that the tree used to beckon to me with his waving arms, and when I was discouraged by my slowness, his

2

leaves seemed to whisper, "Come on, little brother. Come higher," and I would then make a fresh try. There was a spiteful bottle-brush growing near me, and he used to laugh at me because I wanted to grow high enough to be near the tree; and he told me that I would never be any taller than he was. But, though he did discourage me at first, when the tree beckoned I took no notice of his remarks, but kept on trying.

When I was tall enough to see past the flowers, I found that the place where I was living was a point of land running out into the sea. On three sides was the beautiful water, and away on the other shores were hundreds and hundreds of trees. I was too far away to see what kind they were, but I knew they were trees. At first, when I saw the water all sparkling and blue in the sunshine, I thought it was the ocean, but afterwards I found out that it was Sydney Harbour, or, as it is sometimes called, Port Jackson. As I grew taller, I was able to look over the heads of the bushes round me, and see the ships and yachts and ferry boats as they passed.

Sometimes the winds would blow very hard from the south, and lash the blue water into white waves, and make all the trees and bushes bend before it, but the big tree sheltered me, and so I was never hurt by the rough wind, though many of the plants about me were broken and blown to the ground. In all weathers, the big tree was a friend to me, shielding me from the great heat in summer, and keeping the biting winds from me in the winter; and every day I loved him more, and longed to be like him.

And so the seasons went round, and when I had felt the joy of spring for the second time, I was quite a tall stripling, about as high as a man. From the time when I was quite young the insects had crawled over my branches and leaves sucking the sweetness from my veins, but it was not until my third springtime that the birds took any notice of me. I had always envied the big tree, because the birds built their nests amongst his leaves, and fed their babies on his branches, and I wished they would build in me, but they had always flown past. But one morning, when the sun was warming up the world after the winter, and I was feeling very happy as I waved my branches in the gentle breeze, I saw two tiny little yellow-breasted birds flying about, from bush to bush. They did not go to any of the tall trees, but seemed to like the saplings best. I watched them as they flew, and longed for them to come and talk to me. Suddenly I noticed them coming towards me, and, to my delight, they flew straight up, and rested on one of my twigs.

3

"This is a new gum," said one, and I felt very excited, for I had not known until then what my name was. I had learned that the big tree was a Red Gum, and when I heard the little birds call me a "gum," I shook with pleasure, for I thought a gum must be something to do with a Red Gum, and I longed to ask them some more about it.

However, the birds seemed so busy looking up and down my branches and leaves, that I was afraid to move or speak, for fear I should frighten them. So I stood perfectly still and waited, and presently, after they had fussed about a good deal, one said to the other,

"I think this will do." And the other replied:—

"Yes, this is the nicest little tree in the bush, and this branch will be a splendid place for a nest."

My sap seemed to stop running when I heard these words, and I trembled in every leaf.

The little tits, for that's what they were, flew off, but, in a short time, they came back with threads of fibre in their beaks, and then the building began.

It was a dear little nest they made, of root fibres and bark, lined with feathers, and ornamented with spider cocoons. At the side was a tiny, tiny hole, so small that you would have wondered however they expected to get in. But they managed to slip through quite easily, and after a while the babies came out. As they were the very first birds that had ever made their home amongst my leaves, of course I was exceedingly interested, and noticed everything they did from the time the first thread was brought, to the day the babies were able to fly about in their clumsy way amongst my branches. Many other birds have built in me since then, but I have never been so interested in any as those first little tits.

They were nice friendly little birds, and used to chatter a good deal, and when I knew them better, I asked them if a "gum" would ever be a Red Gum. But they laughed, and said they didn't know the answer to that riddle. So I didn't think it any use asking them anything more, for they really seemed too small to have much sense.

When the babies were strong enough to find food for themselves, they all left me, and used to fuss about in the big trees looking for insects, and I never saw much more of them.

While the little tits were living in me, I noticed that several much larger birds had made their homes in the big tree, and I used to hear them singing. This

4

made me envious, for, though the tits chattered and fussed a great deal, they did not sing, and I thought it was because I was so small that the song birds did not come near me.

"I will grow big," I said to myself, "I must be as tall as the big tree!" And I made such an effort to stretch myself, that I could feel the blood in me rising, and I really felt that I was growing taller, and my heart throbbed with happiness. All through the spring and summer I had this glad feeling, but in the autumn I grew tired, and felt as if I must rest, and the sap did not run so quickly. I observed that the other plants and trees about me all looked sad and dark as the autumn came, and I wondered if they were feeling the same as I was. I grew very discouraged, and thought I must really have stopped growing, and that I would never, never get near to my beloved big tree. But his branches kept on beckoning, and his leaves still seemed to whisper messages to me, telling me to "try and try and try." So when the winter was over, I made still another start, and again the sap sprang up, and my tips grew rosy with pleasure at the knowledge that I was still growing.

That spring some native canaries made their long hanging nests in me, and I loved them as I had never thought of loving the little tits, for they used to sing the sweetest songs to me, and I knew that I must be bigger. They were such gentle little birds, and seemed to have more sense than the tits, so I asked them if a "gum" would ever be the same as a Red Gum, but they did not know.

And so the years passed by, and every spring I felt my strength grow greater, and every year the flowers below seemed further away, and the big tree seemed nearer, so I knew I must be growing taller. And every spring the birds came to build in my branches; many different ones they were, Jacky Winters, yellow-bobs, thickheads, and honeyeaters, and each one that lived in me, I asked the same question, "Would a 'gum' ever be a Red Gum?" but none of them knew.

At last, one year, when I was almost as tall as the big tree himself, though not so broad, two peewees came to build their mud nest on one of my branches. They were so much larger than any of the other birds I had met, that I felt they must know more, so I asked them my question, "Would a 'gum' ever be a Red Gum?"

They did not answer immediately, and I shook with excitement as I waited for their reply. Then one said:—

"Maybe!" and the other said "Maybe not!"

5

I thought this a very queer reply, so I said politely: —

"I'm afraid I do not understand. Would you mind explaining?"

"Certainly," they said together; and then one went on in a loud screeching voice:—

"A gum may be a red gum, or it may never be one. It may be a blue gum, or a white gum, or a grey gum, or a blackbutt, or a woollybutt, or a stringy bark, or an iron bark; and then, again, it may be a mahogany, or a fever tree, or a bloodwood, or——"

He stopped for breath, and the other went on:—

"In fact, it seems to us that there are very few things in Australia that a gum can't be!"

If the other birds had known nothing, the peewees certainly knew too much. I was filled with despair when I heard how many different things a gum could be without being a red gum. I did not want to be any of them. All I desired was to be just like my dear, beautiful, big, Red Gum tree. So I was too sad to ask the peewees any more questions just then.

However, in a few days I felt better, and I asked them if they thought I would ever be a Red Gum. They looked me up and down for a while, then one said:—

"Maybe," and the other said "Maybe not!" I was too disgusted by their silly replies to ask them any more questions, for I felt sure then that, though they talked so much, they really knew very little. I have learned since that is always the way in this world. Those people that make the most commotion, and say the most, are usually the ones that do and know the least.

After my disappointment with the peewees, I gave up questioning the birds, and I made up my mind that the only thing to do was to ask the big tree himself. I felt quite certain he would know, but he was too far away for me to speak to him.

"I must go nearer," I said to myself, "I must go nearer!" And so I began to try to stretch my arms across to the big tree. I felt that I was tall enough, so I used all my strength to broaden my branches, and gradually I grew nearer and nearer.

That summer some picnic parties came for the first time to sit on the grass beneath me, as I had often seen them in the shade of the big tree. That made me very proud, for I felt that I, too, must cast a good shadow, and that is a sign of breadth.

But it was in the following spring that I really found out what I was.

6

It was a glorious sunny day; the light breeze was rustling through my leaves and playing hide and seek in my branches. All round me the birds were singing or working at their nests; below me was a carpet of bright flowers, pink, and white, and yellow; and, best of all, the big tree was so near that I could almost touch him, and I knew that I should very soon now be able to ask him my question.

By and by, I noticed that the birds were flying off, as if disturbed, and looking down I saw two men standing below me. In their hands they carried little black boxes, and funny folded stools. They were looking out across the harbour, talking, and I heard one say:—

"I shall paint the little glimpse across the bay, with the boat in the foreground." And the other said:—

"Yes, that's good, but I shall make a sketch of this big Red Gum. I don't know when I saw a finer specimen."

I grew hot with pleasure, for I thought it must be my dear big tree they were talking about, and I looked down to see what kind of men they were to speak so nicely.

Never shall I forget my feeling, when I saw that the man who was speaking had turned his back to the big tree, and was pointing straight at me!

I felt so faint that I could scarcely hold my branches up, and then I heard him say:—

"See the graceful bend in those branches, and what beautiful leaves. The old one there," pointing to my big companion, "is very fine, but this fellow is really magnificent."

I could hardly believe my ears. To think that I was not only a Red Gum, but that these men should call me "magnificent," and finer than the big tree. In all the wildest dreams of my youth, I had never dreamed of that. I was ashamed to look at the big tree, for fear he should be hurt, and I almost wished the men hadn't come.

But suddenly I felt the wind springing up, and as I bent my head before it, my outer leaf clumps touched the swaying branches of the big tree, and I heard him whisper:—

"Well done, little brother! You deserve your reward, for you have been brave. Although you started life as that tiny green point, I soon knew you would rise to great things. I have watched you try, grow disappointed, and try again; and I often longed to help you. You did not know that you would ever become a Red Gum, and yet you kept on trying, and now you are the finest tree in the bush, and I am proud of my brother."

Then my joy was complete; and ever since I have been the happiest tree in the world. And when I hear the young plants grumbling, and giving up hope of ever being tall, I tell them my story, and how by trying I grew from a single green point to be the finest Red Gum in the bush.

THE LEAF THAT LONGED TO BE RED

THERE was once a very discontented Leaf. He lived on a large spreading Sassafras tree in the thick shade of the beautiful brush, where the tall tree-ferns stretched their slender arms towards him, and the maiden-hair ferns grew thick upon the ground. The birds sang in the branches above his head, and the butterflies danced round him. In fact, it was the most delightful place for any leaf to live, and yet this Leaf was as unhappy as if he lived in a city park where the dust soiled and the smoke suffocated.

And the whole reason of his unhappiness was this—he wanted to be red. He was a brilliant shining green, the very prettiest colour a leaf can be, and yet nothing would suit this silly fellow but that he must be red.

He was a very young Leaf, and had been green all his life. He had always been contented until one day some American people had sat beneath his tree and talked, and he heard one say:—

"This is a beautiful bit of bush, but what a pity there is no red or yellow to show up the green." And another answered—

"Yes, if only there were some red leaves like those on the maples in our country, it would be perfect."

And then they went on to say how pretty red leaves were, and how nice they were to decorate with, and how sweet they looked in vases on the table, until the Leaf longed to be one of these wonderful red leaves of which people thought so much, and he felt quite sad and miserable that he was just ordinary bright green.

9

"Do the leaves here never turn red?" asked one of the Americans; and someone answered—

"I believe some do in the autumn, but only a few."

The Leaf heard, and in his heart a hope sprang up. Why shouldn't he be one of the few? He was as large as any of his brothers on the tree, and had just as much right to receive this special honour as any other. He made up his mind to find out who turned some of the leaves red, and then to ask if he might be amongst the favoured ones.

So he asked an old Staghorn, which lived close by, who it was that painted the leaves red in the autumn, and the Staghorn replied—

"Mother Nature. She comes with her paint pot in April and May, and dabs a spot of colour here and there, sometimes red and sometimes yellow. But I really think she must love green best of all, for she lets most of the trees remain that colour. I am glad to say she never disturbs my beautiful blue-green leaves with any of her bright paints."

"But wouldn't you like to be red?" asked the Leaf.

"Certainly not," replied the Staghorn. "I am quite satisfied to be as I am."

But the Leaf was far from being satisfied. All day he wondered when Mother Nature would come, and he was afraid to sleep at night for fear he should miss her, for he intended to ask her to paint him red.

He thought so much about it that he forgot to drink in the dew and rain, and even forgot to lean forward to catch the sunbeams as they flickered through the tall branches overhead. Day and night he thought about becoming red, and how beautiful he would look then, and how people would admire him, and he began to fret and worry more and more each day, for fear he should miss Mother Nature.

Again and again he asked the Staghorn when she would come, and each time the Staghorn told him the same thing—"In the autumn."

But at last the Staghorn grew tired of always being asked the same question, and refused to answer. Then the Leaf asked, "When does autumn come?" and the Staghorn replied, "At the end of the summer."

"Is it nearly the end of the summer yet?" asked the Leaf.

"No; I'm very glad to say it is not," replied the Staghorn, rather sharply, for he wanted to be quiet and enjoy the breeze and sunshine, and the Leaf disturbed his peace with his continual questions.

"Don't you long for the autumn?" asked the Leaf.

10

Mother Nature touched the branches here and there

"No!" answered the Staghorn, curtly.

Then the Leaf saw that the Staghorn did not want to talk any more, so he left off asking questions for a while.

But though he did not speak about the autumn, he did not for a moment forget it. As the days passed, he became more and more anxious to see Mother Nature, and ask her to paint him red; and he spent his time in imagining how fine he would look on a table, for the Americans said they put their red and yellow leaves in vases. He thought it would be much grander to live in a vase than on a tree; and he was so excited at the idea that he did not bother to take his food properly, and he did not eat the sweet juices of his mother tree or drink in the fresh rains and dews. And so he began to grow pale, and to lose his bright green colour, and he felt strangely tired. Then, as the days passed, he grew more and more dissatisfied, until at last there really was not a more discontented leaf in the whole of the bush.

The weather had been intensely hot, and the trees and ferns were all feeling tired, and wishing for the cooler days. Out of the ground rose moist, warm vapours, which made everything feel sticky and damp. Then one night the weather suddenly changed, and there was a fresh, cool feeling in the breeze.

The old Staghorn looked up to the Leaf as soon as it was light, and said—"Autumn has come."

The Leaf trembled with excitement as he said eagerly, "Has it, really? And will Mother Nature soon come now?"

"Yes," replied the Staghorn. "She should be here to-day."

The Leaf was too excited to speak, and he just sat and shook on his twig. Then he heard the Staghorn say in a surprised, eager tone, "Why, here she comes now!"

The Leaf turned to where the Staghorn was pointing, and there, coming through the bushes, was a tall and beautiful woman. Her eyes were bright and brown, and her hair was the colour of ripe corn. She wore a ruddy brown gown, the colour of a russet apple, and in her hand she carried a golden pail filled with a red and yellow mixture

"She is robed in her autumn clothes," said the Staghorn; "and has the paint in her pail. She must be going to begin to-day."

Even as he spoke, Mother Nature stopped before a tall gum tree, and, stretching up her arm, put a splash of colour on some leaves. The Leaf saw that they at once lost their blue shade, and become a light yellow. Then Mother

12

THE LEAF THAT LONGED TO BE RED

Nature came along towards the Leaf, touching branches here and there as she passed, and leaving a red or yellow spot of colour wherever her brush had rested. At last she reached the Leaf's tree, looked at it for a second, and was just going to pass by, when she heard a voice say—

"Please don't go. Won't you paint me, too?"

She looked round in surprise, and saw the Leaf gazing anxiously at her as he repeated—"Please, please paint me, too!"

"Oh, no, dear. I couldn't paint you," said Mother Nature, kindly. "You are too young."

"Ah, no, I'm not. I'm quite grown up, and I do want to be painted red."

"But why, my child?"

"Because red leaves are the most beautiful, and people put them into vases, and I want to live in a vase, and——"

The Leaf stopped for breath, and Mother Nature replied, sadly—

"Ah, yes, red leaves are indeed beautiful, but a leaf must suffer very much before it becomes red, and then it often lies on the ground for days before it is picked up and put into a vase."

"I don't mind how much I suffer, or if I do have to lie on the ground. I'm not afraid of pain. Oh, if only I could be red!"

"But you are too young to suffer, my child."

"No, no, I'm not. I don't mind how you hurt me, if only you will paint me red. Oh, please say you will," and the Leaf stretched eagerly out and touched her hand.

Mother Nature smiled sadly, as she answered:

"Very well, my child. Since you long so much to be red, you shall have your wish. But I hope you won't be sorry afterwards."

"Oh, no; I'll only be happy," cried the Leaf. "I'm not a bit frightened of pain."

Then Mother Nature dipped her brush into her pail, and splashed it right into the Leaf's face.

For a moment he felt as if he were choking, and he could not see. All through his body fire seemed to be rushing, and the pain was terrific.

"Oh, oh, oh!" he cried, and turned to Mother Nature to ask her to take away this terrible feeling. But when he was able to clear the paint from his eyes, so that he could see, she was out of sight. He bent as far forward as he could, but it was no use. She had vanished.

After a little while the pain grew less, and he thought to himself, "Oh, well; I'll soon be all right. I am changing colour already, and I expect by the time I am quite red, I shall be perfectly well again."

But each day, instead of feeling better, he seemed to become weaker and weaker. He no longer felt as if fire was rushing through his veins, but as if all his blood was ebbing away. He was strangely drowsy, too, and wanted to sleep all the time. He took no notice of the birds that flew above his head, and he didn't answer when his old friend the Staghorn spoke to him. He didn't even seem to mind whether he was red or not. All he wanted to do was to sleep.

One day, as he was feeling more than usually drowsy, he was suddenly awakened by voices beneath him, and, as he looked round, he saw a girl pointing to him, and heard her say—"What a pretty red leaf!"

In an instant he was wide awake. He forgot to be tired; forgot he was ill— all he thought of was that at last he was red. At last he would be carried into a house, and live in a vase and decorate a table. Oh, how happy he was! He jumped with joy, and in a moment he had shaken himself free from his twig, and was floating through the air.

Softly and slowly he sank till he reached the earth at the girl's feet.

He lay there trembling with excitement, waiting for her to pick him up and carry him to her house. But he waited in vain, for the girl was gazing at the old Staghorn, and had quite forgotten the Leaf, and though he lay quite close to her foot, she did not notice him, and in a little while she walked on, leaving him alone.

The Leaf could not understand it at all. He did not want to lie on the ground; he wanted to live in a vase, but he did not know how he was to reach one. He knew people put red leaves in vases, and yet this girl had not taken him.

There he lay, however, all that night, and all the next day, but no one else passed him. All round him other leaves were lying, but they were a queer brown colour, which the Leaf had never seen before; and they rustled in a strange manner, and when the Leaf spoke to them they did not answer. They were poor dead leaves, but he did not know that, and thought they were unkind not to speak to him.

As the second day passed into night, he felt very sad and lonely, and he wished he was back on the tree with his brothers. The old Staghorn was ever so high above his head, too far to hear him, and the maiden-hair ferns which were close by were whispering to themselves all the time, and took no notice of him; so there was no one at all for the Leaf to talk to, and he was very miserable.

Then, just as the sun was sinking behind the Sassafras trees, he heard a gentle rustling, and, turning, he saw Mother Nature walking towards him.

"Oh, dear Mother Nature," he cried, "take me home to my branch. I don't like being on the ground, and I am so miserable."

"You shouldn't be miserable," said Mother Nature. "You are now a most lovely red leaf, and if you wait long enough, perhaps someone will pick you up and put you into a vase."

"I don't want to be in a vase. I only want to be back on my tree. Dear Mother Nature, take me back!"

But Mother Nature shook her head, and answered, sadly—

"There is no going back, my child. You wanted to be red, and you said you did not mind pain. You have had your own way, and I cannot alter things now. If you had been content to remain green, you would have lived on your tree for years. I did not want to paint you, and tried to persuade you to stay green; but you would not be happy until I touched you with my paint brush, so I did as you asked."

The poor Leaf grew sadder and sadder as she spoke, and when she had ceased, he felt a strange cold shiver strike through his veins, and he cried—"Oh, if only I had been satisfied!"

But before he could say another word, he rolled over lifeless, and there he lay, a sad, dead Leaf.

Then Mother Nature, with tears in her eyes, took a handful of soft warm earth, and placed it over him.

THE BIRDS' CONCERT

THERE was a great commotion down in the gully. The birds were flying backwards and forwards among the palms and tree ferns. They were all chattering and twittering together, for it was the first day of Spring, which they were going to celebrate by a concert.

It had been rather a severe Winter, and the soft feeling of the Spring day was so delightful to the birds that they flew hither and thither, telling each other gaily "Spring is here, Spring is here."

They nearly all had bright new coats, having got rid of their old ones during the Winter, and as they all met together at the bottom of the gully where the concert was to be held, they made a beautiful picture.

The Emu was presiding; as he was the largest of the birds, he was always the chairman on occasions of this kind. He stood beneath a tall gum-tree, and in front of him was a clear space where the performers were to stand. On the other side of this space the birds sat in a circle. There were all kinds there, big and small, pretty and plain, and they all looked as happy as they could be, for birds dearly love the Spring.

The Emu stretched his long neck, and looked round with his big, bright eyes, to see that everyone was ready to begin; then he said:

"I think we should open with a chorus."

"Yes, yes, a chorus," shouted the birds, and then, all standing up together, they sang with all their hearts this Spring song—

"Spring is here! Spring is here!
And the skies are blue and clear.
Winter with its cold is past,
And the summer's coming fast.

"Spring is here! Spring is here!
Flowers are opening everywhere.
New buds sprout upon the trees,
Butterflies float in the breeze.

"Spring is here! Spring is here!
Each bird calls unto his dear,
'Little mate, I love you best,
Come with me and build a nest.'"

THE BIRDS' CONCERT

It was a song they sang every Spring, and so they all knew it by heart, and sang it very well.

When they had finished, they went back to their places, and waited for the next item.

The Emu cleared his throat, and said: "I have not drawn up a regular programme, but I think the best singer should begin."

"Yes, yes, certainly," cried several birds.

"But, unfortunately," went on the Emu, "I am not able to decide who is the best singer. I myself do not profess to sing, but I know that several of you have very good voices, and I think the best way would be for us to decide now which is the finest singer, and then he can sing. I will give you three minutes to think it over, and then you can tell me which one you have chosen."

For three minutes after he had finished speaking there was not a sound except the whispering of the birds among themselves. Then the Emu said:

"Time's up!"

Immediately there broke forth such a noise and confusion that it sounded like some horrible fight. Every bird was calling out the name of the one it thought the best singer, and each name was different. There were cries of Reed Warbler, Jacky Winter, Butcher Bird, Bell Bird, Magpie, Lyre Bird, Native Canary, Tomtit, Wagtail, Cocktail, and a dozen other names.

"Order, order!" shrieked the Emu; "this will never do. I did not dream there would be so much difference of opinion. Clearly we must find some other way of deciding."

"Surely there is no need to decide. There can be no possible doubt about the matter; I am the best singer."

The speaker was the Lyre Bird, and he stalked into the centre with his long tail proudly lifted above his back.

"Indeed you're not the best singer," cried several birds angrily; "you're only a mimic."

The Lyre Bird just ignored them, and waved his tail scornfully as he said to the Emu, "Shall I begin?"

The Emu did not approve of the Lyre Bird's conceited manner, so he said:

"No; I think we must prove which is the best singer by a competition. All those birds who have good voices must each sing a song, and the Parrot, the Cockatoo, and I shall decide which is the best."

"Why should the Parrot and the Cockatoo judge?" asked the Lyre Bird. "They can't sing."

"That is the reason why they will make good judges, for they will be unprejudiced."

"It seems to me a most foolish waste of time," went on the Lyre Bird, "for you must agree in the end that I am the best singer."

"I think your talking is the greatest waste of time," interrupted a Peewee. "Do be quiet and let us begin."

The Lyre Bird did not answer, but walked away with his tail raised in a most disdainful fashion.

"Let all those birds that are going to compete, step into the front row," called the Emu.

Immediately about thirty birds hopped in front of the others, and stood in a row. They were of all sorts and sizes, some were large, some small, some brightly coloured, some plain brown, and they all looked very eager to begin.

"I think it would be best to commence with the smallest, and go on by turns to the biggest," said the Emu, "and each bird must step into the centre alone as he sings. Now let the smallest begin."

Instantly there stepped forward a small bird in a beautiful coat of black and blue, with a long tail raised above his back. It was the Blue Wren, or, as he is sometimes called, the Cocktail. He threw his head back and began to sing in a gushing voice:

"I'm a Cocktail, small and perky
And I hop with action jerky.
Tho' my song is small I fear,
It is very sweet to hear."

Before he had finished there was a rustling noise, and the Lyre Bird hurried up into the centre. He stood in front of the tiny Blue Wren, and lifting his head and tail in the same manner as the small bird, began to mimic him. He sang the same words in the same way, but his voice was richer and fuller, and it sounded as if there were several Blue Wrens singing in chorus.

The Blue Wren was most indignant, but the other birds couldn't help laughing, for it was such an absurd sight.

"No hope for you, young Cocktail," called out the Parrot, and the little bird hopped back to his place dejectedly.

The next bird to sing was the Silvereye, and he sang a sad little song in a very sweet, low voice, which sounded rather like that of a canary:

> "A lonely little bird am I,
> Whom people call the Silvereye.
> I really wish I could be glad,
> But as a rule I'm very sad.
> Pee-ek, pee-e-ek, pee-e-ek."

"A very pretty little song, and nicely sung," said the Emu, but he was interrupted by the Lyre Bird, who in an exact imitation of the Silvereye, sang:

> "A silly little bird are you,
> And no one cares what you may do.
> And tho' you pose as being shy,
> I think you're really very sly.
> Chee-ek, chee-ek, chee-ek!"

"Order, order," cried the Emu, "really, Lyre Bird, I am surprised at your bad manners. You ought to know better."

But the Lyre Bird only laughed scornfully and danced round the circle.

"Don't take any notice of him," said the Cockatoo, "let us go on to the next."

"I'm the next," said a small bird who was known as the Native Canary, though his voice was not as much like a canary as was the Silvereye's. Still, it was very sweet and clear. He began on a high note, and his song went down like a musical scale, sounding like this:

```
Down,                          To
   down,                          like
      I                              my
         go                              song
            right                            you
               down                              can-
                  the                               not
                     scale.                            fail.
```

In a second the Lyre Bird had begun to imitate him, and he sang:

<pre>
        That   As
         you   vain
          are   as
         vain   an-
          we   y
        plain-   bird
          ly   could
            see,   be.
</pre>

By this time the other birds had ceased to be amused and were all really annoyed. They began to complain to each other, saying that it was disgraceful, and that the Lyre Bird ought to be ashamed of himself.

"It's only because we're small that you mock us," shouted the Blue Wren. "You wouldn't dare to do so if we were big, you bully."

"He couldn't imitate us if he dared," said the Magpie, who was one of the biggest birds.

"Couldn't I?" sneered the Lyre Bird, "just wait and see."

The Parrot and the Cockatoo were talking excitedly to the Emu, as if they were making suggestions, and at last the Emu nodded his head in approval; then he said in a loud voice:

"As the judges, we have decided that the best singer shall be the one whom this rude Lyre Bird cannot imitate."

"That's a very good plan," said several of the birds, and so it was agreed, and the competition went on.

But though several birds sang entirely different songs in entirely different voices, the Lyre Bird mimicked them all. And the worst of it was that, although his voice was like the one he imitated, his tones were fuller than any of theirs. The Tomtit, Jacky Winter, Willy Wagtail, and Blackcap, having all sung and been mocked, retired in anger. Then there flew into the centre a slim, olive-brown bird. There was nothing very striking in his appearance, but when he began to sing, his first notes proclaimed him something out of the common.

He was a Reed Warbler, and this was his song:

> "On the reeds of the creek do I swing,
> As I sing, as I sing.
> While the winds whistle soft in the grass,
> As they pass, as they pass.

THE BIRDS' CONCERT

"And the waters wash softly and sweet
   At my feet, at my feet.
No bird is more joyful than I
   'Neath the sky, 'neath the sky.

"But I'm not only happy and gay
   In the day, in the day,
For I sing with a wondrous delight
   All the night, all the night."

He sang with a clear, sweet, thrilling voice, which delighted every ear. As he finished, there was a burst of applause from his listeners.

"Surely the Lyre Bird will not try to imitate that," said the Magpie. But he did not know the limits of the Lyre Bird's impudence, for as soon as the applause had died away, the mimic began. He could not remember all the words of the Reed Warbler's song, so he whistled the air in the very same way. But this time the imitation was not better than the original; indeed, it was scarcely as good. Still it was an imitation, and so it could not be said that the Reed Warbler had won the competition.

Then there flew down two very beautiful birds. One had a glorious yellow breast, with a black collar and head, and a white throat. The other was just the same, except that his breast was red instead of yellow. They were both Thickheads, or Thunder Birds, and two of the most beautiful of all the birds. Side by side they stood, and in rich, round voices they sang:

"In open scrub or thickest brush,
   We may be found;
And into song we always rush
   At any sound.

"Report of gun or thunder heard
   Brings forth our song;
And so we're known as Thunderbird,
   E-cheu, e-chong!"

Their voices were even more clear and loud than the Reed Warbler's. though they could not sing so long; and the last two words, "E-cheu, e-chong," were sung in a queer way which sounded very like the cracking of a whip.

But though their song was beautiful, sad to say it was very easy to imitate, and the Lyre Bird danced up and down saying "e-cheu, e-chong," over and over again.

He ran away as fast as his legs would carry him

Still the birds did not despair, and one after another they sang. Each one came up hoping the Lyre Bird could not imitate him, and each one went back disappointed and angry, as he heard his music mocked. At last there were only three song birds left to sing—The Bell Bird, the Butcher Bird, and the Magpie. The Bell Bird's song was this:

"Ding, dong, ding, dong!
Listen to the Bell Birds song.
You can hear it far and near,
Ringing out so loud and clear,
Ding, ding, ding."

This the Lyre Bird mimicked with the greatest ease.

Then the Butcher Bird sang his song:

"They call me Butcher Bird,
A name which suits me well;
For little birds I chase and kill
And carry off within my bill,
As anyone can tell."

And again the Lyre Bird mimicked.

"Only one more," said the Emu. "Surely, Magpie, you can sing something too hard for this impudent fellow to copy."

"I'll try," said the Magpie, and in a deep, rich contralto voice, he sang:

"Quite early in the morning I awake,
And pour my song out to the coming day.
Across the paddocks you can hear my voice,
Gurgling and gay."

But, alas, though his voice was quite unlike that of any of the other birds, it was just as easy for the Lyre Bird to imitate. He did so, running up and down with his tail spread high, and rejoicing to see the Magpie's dismay.

"Ah, ah, so you thought I could not imitate you, Mister Magpie," he cried. "Your song was to be too good for me to copy. Listen to this," and in a deep contralto voice, just like the Magpie's, he sang:

"The Magpie is a very cunning fowl,
Who gets up early—so you've heard him say,
And eats the food of all the other birds,
While they're away."

"How do you like that, Mister Magpie?"

23

"Shame, shame!" cried several birds, for the Magpie himself was too angry to speak. But the Lyre Bird ignored them, and turning to the Emu, said:

"Now, Mister President, I think you must admit that I am the best singer."

Before the Emu could answer, the Parrot said quickly: "But there are still plenty of birds you haven't imitated. Let them compete."

"Yes," said the Emu, "the true songsters have all sung and been mimicked; now let the other birds try."

"Oh, very well," replied the Lyre Bird, "I have no objection, though it is a terrible waste of time."

"However, it shall be done," said the Emu sternly.

So the other birds, who do not profess to sing, came and made songs. There were Parrots, Cockatoos, Catbirds, Peewees, Black Magpies, Woodpeckers, and many others. Many of them just gave several loud shrieks, which the Lyre Bird immediately echoed. But the Black Magpie sang a real song. In a loud clanging voice he shouted:

> "Come-along, come-along, come-along!
> Come-along, Mister Lyre Bird, and try,
> If, without going wrong, you can mimic the song
> Of the wonderful Black Magpie.
> Come-along, come-along!"

"Pooh! do you really believe I can't imitate that?" and the Lyre Bird at once began to shriek:

> Get-along, get-along, get-along!
> Do you really believe I need try
> To mimic your song? Why an old broken gong
> Could mimic the Black Magpie.
> Get-along, get-along."

The Black Magpie was the last. All the birds had sung—big and little, young and old, those with voices, those with none—and the Lyre Bird had mocked them all. They all looked very miserable, and not a bit like the same happy birds that had sung their spring chorus. The Emu looked worried, the Parrot and the Cockatoo looked very cross, and the only one that looked happy was the Lyre Bird. With mincing steps he danced round the circle, bowing mockingly to each bird as he passed. Then he stopped before the Emu, and said in a most conceited voice:

"Surely you are satisfied now that I am the best singer. Not one of those stupid birds can sing a song that I cannot copy. Whether they sing or shriek, I can mimic them all."

24

"Not quite all," said a voice overhead.

Everyone looked up, and there on a branch sat the Kookaburra, whom everyone had forgotten.

"You haven't mimicked me yet," said the Kookaburra.

"You didn't sing," objected the Lyre Bird.

"No, I have been enjoying the fun, and it has amused me so much that I can now laugh heartily. Will you try to copy me, Lyre Bird?"

"Of course I can copy you. There is no need to try."

"Very well. Listen carefully;" and Kookaburra threw his funny long bill into the air, and began:

> "A laughing Jack am I.
> Ha-ha, ha-ha, ha-ha!
> I laugh away, I laugh all day,
> I laugh both low and high.
> Ha-ha, ha-ha, ha-ha, ha-ha, ha-ha-ha,
> Ha-ha-hah!"

As he began to sing in his queer laughing gurgle, the Lyre Bird's face lost its mocking smile, and became very long, and the longer the Kookaburra laughed, the longer the Lyre Bird's face grew, till finally it was as long as his tail.

At last the Kookaburra stopped, and the other birds all cried out:

"Mimic that, copy-cat, if you can!"

The Lyre Bird felt far from laughing, but he began his imitation of the Kookaburra. "Ha, ha, ha, ha."

He could get no further. Though he stretched his throat to the utmost, and strained his lungs, he could not make a laugh like the Kookaburra's. Again and again he tried, but in vain. He could not get beyond the first two notes.

Then all the other birds shouted and screeched with joy, and the Kookaburra cried:

"Ah, Mister Lyre Bird, who's the best singer now?" and then he burst out laughing again.

But this was too much for the Lyre Bird. He could not bear to be laughed at, although he had made such fun of the others, so he just turned his back, and ran away as fast as his legs could carry him.

And to this day you will never find the Lyre Bird with other birds. He plays only with his own brothers; and in the deep gullies you will often hear him mimicking all the birds in the bush, except the Kookaburra; for even yet he can only copy the first few notes of that strange laugh.

When he had gone the Kookaburra said:

"I suppose I have won the competition, although as you all know I can't sing a note. So I propose, Mister President, we do not bother about who is the best singer, but let us finish up with a general chorus."

So they all sang together:

"We're all very happy little birds,
And it doesn't matter who sings best,
    The Lyre Bird's away,
    But he's wasted all the day,
And the sun now is sinking in the west.

"So no matter who may sing the finest song,
To do our best the whole of us will try.
    If the music of our voice
    Makes a single heart rejoice,
We'll be satisfied; and now we say 'good-bye.' "

THE COCKTAILS' PARTY

MR. and Mrs. Cocktail were going to give a party to celebrate the coming of age of their only son, Bluetip. There was a great deal of talk about it amongst the other birds, who were all anxious to know who was to be asked, and each one hoped he would receive an invitation, for the Cocktails had such a splendid home for a party. By the way, I must tell you that birds do not live in their nests, as so many of you think. In the spring they build nests in which to lay their eggs, and bring up their babies, but, as soon as the children are able to fly, the nests are deserted, and the families live amongst the branches of trees and shrubs.

Now, the Cocktails lived under a low wide-spreading cassia, which every spring was covered with golden flowers, so they decided to wait till their house was in full bloom before they had the party. Already the tree was in bud, and it only needed a few days' sunshine to make it burst into a mass of beautiful golden blossoms. So the Cocktails began to prepare.

It was decided to hold the party at break of day, before any people began to come about, and on this point the whole family was agreed. But when they came to sending out the invitations, the disagreements began.

Mr. Cocktail wrote out the card as he thought it should be, and this is what he put:—

> MR. AND MRS. COCKTAIL
> request the pleasure of your company
> on Friday morning to celebrate the
> coming of age of their son, Bluetip.
> Dancing and Singing.
> R.S.V.P.

"Very nice," said his wife; "but, of course, my dear, you would not write 'Cocktail.' It should be 'Mr. and Mrs. Blue Wren.' You know Cocktail is a very vulgar name."

"But all the birds know us by that name, and so do all children. It is only grown-up humans who call us 'Blue Wrens.'"

"I don't care. 'Cocktail' is vulgar, and I will have the cards written 'Blue Wren,'" and the little lady shook her tail most furiously.

"Very well, my dear," said her husband, "to please you I shall write 'Blue Wren,' but I trust our neighbours will not laugh at us."

Just then up hopped their son, young Bluetip. "What are you doing?" he asked, and his mother handed him the card.

He read it through, then burst out laughing. "Oh, mother," he cried, "you can't call yourselves 'Cocktail' on a card!"

"Just what I said," exclaimed his mother. "But your father has agreed to alter it to 'Blue Wren.' I told him 'Cocktail' was common."

"Blue Wren?" echoed Bluetip. "Oh, no, mother. That is just as bad."

"Well, what shall we be, if you don't like 'Blue Wren?'" asked his mother, sharply.

"Why, 'Superb Warbler,' of course," said Bluetip, grandly.

"Superb what?" shrieked his mother, while his father burst out laughing.

"You need not laugh," said Bluetip, indignantly: "that is our proper name."

"Wherever did you hear it?" asked his father, when he was able to speak for laughing.

"That's what the man at the Museum calls us, and he knows everything about birds. I heard him myself. I was standing underneath that big kurrajong tree singing, and he passed by with another man, and said, 'There is a young Superb Warbler.' So that must be our right name."

Mr. Cocktail look puzzled. "I never heard the name before, and yet the man at the Museum knows everything. It's very strange, very strange."

"I understand," suddenly cried Mrs. Cocktail, in a very excited voice. Didn't you say you were singing, Bluetip?"

"Yes, mother."

"Then that is why he called you a 'Superb Warbler.' It was because he heard your lovely voice, my son, for 'Superb Warbler' means 'beautiful singer.'"

The little mother shook with pride, for she was quite certain that the man at the Museum must have admired Bluetip's voice very much indeed to call him by such a name.

Mr. Cocktail wagged his head approvingly. "That's it, my dear," he said: "you are quite right. I never heard the name before, so it must be because of our child's voice," and they both looked fondly at their son.

Young Bluetip drew himself up proudly, and, lifting his head, burst into song.

"That's it, that's it," cried the two delighted parents; "he is indeed a Superb Warbler."

And so it was settled that the invitations should be sent out from Mr. and Mrs. Superb Warbler. Mr. Cocktail feebly raising a slight objection by saying, "But it is our son's name, not ours, my dear." But his wife quickly answered—

"A son's name is the same as his parents', so the parents' must be the same as the son's!" and as Mr. Cocktail had nothing to answer to that, the invitations were written.

Then came a discussion as to which birds should be invited. Bluetip wished to ask all the birds in the Gardens, for he wanted everyone to hear him sing his birthday song. But his parents would not agree to that.

"We won't ask any big birds, for they eat too much," said Mrs. Cocktail.

"Yes, and they get in the way and want to order everyone about," said Mr. Cocktail, who always liked to be the most important person in any group of birds.

When the list was finished, these were the birds to be asked:—Yellowbobs, Jacky Winters, Tomtits, Little Tits, Silvereyes, Spinebills, Chickups, Bloodbirds, Diamond Dicks, Mistletoe Birds, Fantails, and Barkpeckers. The Peewees were too big; the Swallows were too flighty; the Budgerigars were too noisy; and the Wagtails could not be asked as guests, for they were coming as waiters.

While they were making out the list, there was great curiosity and excitement amongst all the birds to know if they would be asked, and a fat Dove sat in the tree next door, and kept calling in a sad voice "Ask me too, ask me too." But the Cocktails only laughed at him, and would not ask him, for he was a foreigner, and Mr. Cocktail didn't like foreigners.

"They come here," he said, "eat all our flies and grubs and seed, and don't let us have a chance."

Of course the Sparrow and Starlings were not put down on the list, for they are greediest and rudest of all the foreigners, and Mr. Cocktail hated them.

But if the birds were excited, and talked before the invitations were sent out, imagine their surprise and gossip when each one received a card from "Mr. and

Mrs. Superb Warbler!" All the small fry collected together to talk the matter over. "Where did they get the name? What does it mean?" they asked each other in wonder. But none of them could answer the question.

At last a Spinebill said, "Let us ask the Kingfisher. He travels a good deal, and may know."

The others agreed that it was a good idea, so they all started off to the pond where the Kingfisher was staying.

He looked very wise as he sat gazing into the water, his beautiful blue coat shining in the sun. But he was very obliging, and when the Spinebill asked him would he be kind enough to explain to them what a "Superb Warbler" was, he at once replied—

"It's the name the man at the Museum gives the Cocktails, and it means beautiful singer."

"What!" cried a Jacky Winter. "Cocktails called beautiful singers! Well, I declare! And he only calls me a Brown Flycatcher. Well, what shall we hear next?"

"Beautiful singer!" said a Tomtit. "Why, they don't sing half so well as I do. Beautiful singer, indeed! Beautiful fiddlesticks!"

This made all the other Tomtits and Little Tits giggle, and they kept on saying "Beautiful fiddlesticks," and then giggling, till Mrs. Yellowbob said to them, "Chut, chut, you youngsters. Don't make so much noise."

"I call it affectation to use that name," said Miss Chickup, pertly; but Mr. Spinebill said, politely—

"No, I think they are quite right, quite right," and several others agreed with him.

But whatever the birds might think about the Cocktails' new name, they all agreed in accepting the invitation to the party, and the answers were sent at once.

At last the morning of the party arrived. The Cocktails were up long before daylight, making the final arrangements, and by the time the first rays of light appeared across the harbour, everything was ready. There were piles of fresh seeds, heaps of juicy berries, and a nice lot of flies and moths and beetles newly caught, so that all their guests should have dishes to their liking. The flowers of the cassia were in full bloom, and made the ballroom the prettiest ever seen, and the Cocktails looked round with satisfied glances.

"Everything is perfect," said Bluetip.

"I don't think anything has been forgotten," said Mrs. Cocktail, anxiously.

"No, everything is there," said Mr. Cocktail.

"Well, now we must get ready," said the mother. So off they all went to the nice soft part of the flower bed, and each had a good dust bath. After their bath they shook their feathers out, and then they were three pretty, clean little birds.

Bluetip looked enviously at his father, whose beautiful coat of brilliant blue and black was shining after the bath.

"I wish I had a coat like father's," he said, wistfully.

His parents looked at each other, and nodded. Then Mrs. Cocktail said:

"Come to the fountain, Bluetip. I have something to show you."

Bluetip followed her across the lawn to the fountain, where his mother hopped up on to the edge. He flew up beside her wondering what was going to happen.

"Look into the water," she said; and Bluetip looked. There he saw his little brown mother, with her blue tail proudly raised above her back, and beside her stood the most beautiful Mr. Cocktail he had ever seen. His coat was of the brightest shining black, trimmed with gleaming blue, and on his head was a cap of the same bright colour. Bluetip was astonished, for he had not seen any other Cocktails about. Then suddenly he understood.

"Is it—is it me?" he gasped.

"Yes, dear, it is you," replied his mother.

"But I don't understand," he said. "I thought I was plain brown, like you, but there I am just like father."

"When you were a little boy you were plain brown," explained his mother, "for brown is the safest colour for children and mothers. It is not easily seen, and so our enemies do not notice the children who are weak, or the mother when she is sitting on her nest. But now you are a strong bird, Bluetip, and able to take care of yourself, so you need not wear your dingy brown coat any longer, but have got this nice blue suit."

"Oh, I am so glad," cried Bluetip. "I have always wanted to have a coat like my father's. I am so happy," and be broke forth into a joyful song.

When he had finished singing, his mother said: "Now, my child, we must go back, for the sun is just coming over South Head, and our guests will be here presently." So they flew back to their home.

The Spinebills were the first of the guests to arrive. Mr. Spinebill flew along in front, calling to his wife, "Be quick, be quick," but he waited for her at the edge of the lawn, and they both arrived at the party together. They bowed politely to their hosts, and said:

"Good morning, Mr. and Mrs. Superb Warbler. Many happy returns of the day, Bluetip." They then went on into the ballroom.

Mrs. Cocktail was delighted. Although they had sent the invitations from the Superb Warblers she had not thought the birds would call her that. She smiled sweetly, and whispered to her husband, "The Spinebills are a nice couple." But before he had time to answer, some more of the guests arrived.

The sedate birds came in pairs—Mr. and Mrs Yellowbob looking very sweet and friendly in their green coats and yellow fronts; Mr. and Mrs. Jacky Winter; and Mr. and Mrs. Barkpecker. Miss Fantail came alone, spreading out her train in a most fashionable manner. Behind her came the Silvereyes, gazing at her through their silver-rimmed eyeglasses.

All these birds advanced politely, and greeted the Cocktails in the same way as the Spinebills had done. But when the Tomtits and Little Tits arrived, all together and very late, they were whispering and giggling amongst themselves. They advanced in a group towards their hosts, each one nudging the other forward to be spokesman. At last a Little Tit said—

"Good-day, Mrs. Superb War——," he could not finish the name, but put his claw to his mouth and spluttered with laughter. Then all the other Tits laughed and giggled more than ever, till Mr. Cocktail was most indignant, and his wife was crying with annoyance.

Kind Mrs. Yellowbob soothed her gently. "Don't mind them, my dear; they are only silly children," she said; so Mrs. Cocktail wiped her eyes and smiled again.

And all the other birds were so friendly and polite that presently the Tomtits and Little Tits felt ashamed, and stopped whispering and sniggering. Then everyone was happy, and the party really began.

They opened with a song, in which Mr. Jacky Winter sang the solo, and all the others joined in the chorus—

"Bluetip, Bluetip,
  You're of age to-day;
We hope that you'll be happy,
  Hooray, Hooray, Hooray!
    Chorus—Hooray, Hooray, Hooray!"

As all the little birds sang with all their might, it sounded very fine.

After the song was finished, Mr. Spinebill delighted the audience with an acrobatic performance. He flew up to the ceiling, and, piercing his long, fine bill into the heart of a cassia flower, hung poised in the air, with his wings quivering, for quite a long time, till all the guests cried, "Wonderful, wonderful." Then several of the others performed in turn; the Jacky Winters caught flies on the wing and chased each other round and round till the others felt quite giddy; the Barkpeckers walked down the branches, head first, till the ladies held up their hands in horror, and cried, "Oh, my; oh, my!" Then, after a great deal of persuasion, Miss Fantail consented to perform her renowned skirt dance, and never was there a prettier sight. The birds applauded so long that Miss Fantail felt quite shy, and all agreed that then she was prettier than ever.

But the event of the morning was Bluetip's song, and it was to be the last thing before breakfast. He had composed it himself, and everyone was anxious to hear him. At last the moment arrived. All the visitors sat round in a semi-circle, and Bluetip faced them. For a moment he felt very shy and strange before so many, till his mother softly chirped to him, "Courage, Bluetip." Then he drew himself up proudly, and with head well back, and chest well forward, he sang this song—

"I'm a year old to-day,
  And I've grown up so fine,
That Mamma and Papa
  Thought they'd ask you to dine.

"There are beetles and flies,
  And everything nice;
The honey and dew
  Have been put on the ice.

"I have a new suit,
And a pretty new cap,
And I'm altogether
A very fine chap.

"So I welcome you all,
From largest to least;
And now I shall ask you
To sit at the feast."

A round of applause broke forth at the end of the song, and then such congratulations to the parents, and such compliments to Bluetip went round, that the three Cocktails simply quivered with pride, and held their tails higher than ever.

And then, when everyone had finished saying pretty things, Mr. Cocktail jumped up on to a bough, and said—

"My dear friends,—We thank you very much for your kindness and your company. And now, will you come and partake of our feast?"

Of course they were all delighted to see the refreshments—though Miss Fantail seemed quite surprised at there being any—and in a few minutes they were seated round the feast. The four Wagtails were kept as busy as they could be, waiting on the guests, and the Cocktails themselves helped to look after their visitors.

Everyone was jolly and happy, and far too much interested in the flies and beetles and seed to notice what was going on outside.

But, alas, alas! there was a great deal going on outside. Suddenly there broke upon the ears of the happy party a sound like a coming hurricane. The day grew strangely dark, and before the guests had time to turn in their seats, the whirring noise was right beside them, and a crowd of Sparrows and Starlings came bursting through the branches, led by the fat Dove.

Oh, what consternation there was! The little birds shrieked with fright, and tried to get out of the way, but before they could move many of them were pounced on by the cruel enemy. Some of the husbands fought valiantly, but they were outnumbered and there was nothing left but to fly. In a few moments there was not one member of the party left, and the greedy Sparrows and Starlings were gobbling up the feast as fast as they could, while the fat Dove, who had stirred them up, and led them to the attack, waved his head, and kept on saying, "Serve them right; they wouldn't ask me."

34

And, oh! the sorrow and sadness of the little birds, as they met at the other end of the Gardens to talk it over!

After much discussion they wrote a letter to the Governor, and told him what they wanted. But whether they ever got an answer, I cannot say, for the Sparrows and Starlings still do their best to gobble up everything and starve the other birds. But perhaps some day they will be punished. I hope so; don't you?

THE DISCONTENTED STREAM

ONCE upon a time a little Stream lived in the beautiful brush country amongst the hills. His banks were bordered by all the brightest and greenest trees of the land; big coachwoods and maiden's-blushes spread their branches above his head; lillipillis with glossy leaves and bright berries, and sassafras with starry blossoms bent over him, and were reflected in his mirror. Giant maiden-hair clustered close to his brink, and tree-ferns and bangalows whispered in the breeze and made his banks more beautiful. In the spring the birds built their nests in the bushes just above him, and he could watch the mother birds sitting on their eggs and the father birds bringing them food; and later on he could see the babies being taken out of the nest and taught to fly. In the summer the birds would come and bathe in his waters, and every evening they would come down to drink. There were satin-birds, thrushes, beautiful big blue pigeons with dull red crests, lovely little green pigeons, black magpies—in fact, all the shy, beautiful birds that live in the brush country.

And yet, with all this beauty round him, he was most discontented. He should have been the happiest stream in the world, for he had no worries or troubles, and nothing ugly to look at. But instead of singing happily as all good little streams do, he did nothing but murmur and mutter all day long. And the reason of his discontent was this.

Right in the centre of the gully along which he ran, there stood a steep, high hill, too high and steep for the Stream to cross over, and he had to turn out of his way and run round. At first he had not minded very much, for he thought he would be able to climb the hill when he grew bigger; but as day after day, and year after year went by, and he still had to run round the foot of the hill, he grew more and more sulky and discontented, until at last he hated the very sight of the hill.

"Great big ugly thing!" he said, as he ran past it, "Why don't you stay up in the mountains instead of coming down into my gully?"

The hill took no notice of his remarks, but held his head high up, and did not even look at the Stream.

All up the hill-slope grew big gum-trees and young gum saplings. Here the bell-birds fed and called from dawn to dark, and never came down to feed among the trees at the Stream's edge. This also made the Stream angry.

"It isn't fair," he said, "that that old hill should have the bell-birds singing all day long, while I have only stupid, silent birds that are too shy to say a word. Why don't you sing?" he exclaimed angrily to a Wonga pigeon, who was drinking on the bank.

"Oh, oh, oh, I like that," said the Wonga. "Why don't you sing yourself, instead of grumbling all day? If you were brighter and happier we should not be so quiet."

"Stupid thing!" said the Stream to himself, "Of course he doesn't understand. He can fly away and get over the top of the hill whenever he likes. If I could only do that I shouldn't be as stupid and dull as he is. I should sing and dance with joy all day."

"Well, come and dance now!" shouted some Sunbeams, rushing down through the leaves of a big fig tree.

"I can't," said the Stream pettishly.

"Why can't you?" asked the Sunbeams.

"Because this place is too dull. If I could only get up to the top of that hill, I should be quite happy and bright, but this place is too dull for me to dance in."

"It's you that are dull," cried the Sunbeams, laughing at him. "Why don't you try to be happy?" Then they danced away amongst the trees, calling out —"We'll come and see you again when you are in a brighter mood."

"It's all very well for them to talk," grumbled the Stream to himself, "they can dance away wherever they want to. They haven't got to run round that old hill all their lives. If they had to stay down here in the valley always they wouldn't laugh and dance like that," and he went grumbling on his way.

A little way along the gully he met a Lyre Bird, who came skipping down the hill and bent over to drink in the Stream's waters.

"Good day," he said in a cheerful voice, "isn't it a glorious morning?"

"H'm!" said the Stream sulkily, "it's not bad."

"Not bad?" echoed the Lyre Bird, "why, whatever more could you want? The weather is just perfect."

"Oh, yes, the weather's all right," grumbled the Stream, "but what's the good of that?"

"Why, it makes one feel so happy and cheerful. I want to sing and dance all the time when the weather is so good. Don't you?"

"No," said the Stream crossly, "I don't."

"Whatever is the matter with you to-day?" asked the Lyre Bird. "Why are you so dull?"

"Dull," shouted the Stream angrily. "Everyone wants to know why I am dull. Well, I'll tell you why. I want to run up that hill, and I can't. There!"

"But Streams never run up hills!"

"I don't care what other Streams do. I know that I am tired of running round that hill all my life. I want to go up the slopes to the top, where the gum-trees and the bell-birds are."

"But," said the Lyre Bird, "there are prettier trees here, and more beautiful birds all along your banks."

"But they don't sing like the bell-birds. They are all so shy and stupid."

"I can sing to you as well as the bell-birds. Indeed I can mimic their notes if you like."

"Yes, but you are not here all the time," said the Stream. "You only stay for a little while and then you go back to the hills. Oh, those hills, they have all the best things!" and the Stream began to weep miserably.

The Lyre Bird felt very sorry for him. He was a kind-hearted bird, and he thought that it must be dull to stay in one place always. He could move from hilltop to valley just as he liked, and when he saw the Stream weeping, he pitied him and began to think what he could do to help him.

"Have you ever tried to climb the hill?" he asked.

"Yes, but I can never get up more than a few feet. I am not big or strong enough."

"Well," said the Lyre Bird, "I am very sorry indeed for you, and I'll try to think of some way of helping you. I shall come back to-morrow and let you know if I succeed," and away he danced up the valley, singing cheerily as he went.

He had been so kind and sympathetic that the Stream felt quite brightened up and was almost gay as he flowed along. There was something in the Lyre Bird's manner that gave him confidence, and he believed that he really might do something to help him up the hill. So he left off grumbling and almost began to sing. And when the birds came down to drink in the evening they all noticed that he was far less unhappy than usual.

"Have you been able to run up the hill?" asked the big blue Pigeon.

They sent the stream up, up, up

"No," said the Stream, "but I think I soon shall. The Lyre Bird has promised to help me."

"Oh," said the Pigeon, "if he helps you, you'll be able to manage it, for he is so clever and can do anything he wants to."

"Can he?" said the Stream eagerly.

"Yes," agreed all the birds. "The Lyre Bird is a very clever fellow, and if anyone can help you he can." And then they all flew off to bed.

All through the night the Stream ran on, thinking of the morrow, and wondering what plan the Lyre Bird would suggest, and he felt so sure and happy that he began to sing a little gentle song, that lulled the birds on their branches, and made them sleep more peacefully.

Early in the morning, as the first sunbeams came stealing up over the hills, the Lyre Bird came dancing down to meet the Stream.

The Stream saw him in the distance, and called out, "Have you thought of anything?"

"Yes!" answered the Lyre Bird, and hurried towards him. "Yesterday when I left you," he said, "I went up into the hills, for I can think better there, and as I went along I suddenly thought I should go and ask the Waterfall if she knew of a way to help you. She was very kind, and listened while I told her your story, and she has promised to help you."

"How?" asked the Stream eagerly.

"When the next big rains come, she has promised to send all her children down to you. They will press you and push you and give you strength, so that you will be quite big and strong enough to go up the side of the hill instead of running round its foot."

"And when will the big rains come?" asked the Stream.

"The Waterfall says they are due now, and may come any day."

"Hurrah, hurrah!" shouted the Stream. "Thank you, thank you for helping me," and he ran gaily down the valley, singing loudly.

And the very next day the rains came. At first just a few odd drops fell, then faster and faster, and thicker and thicker they came, hundreds and thousands and millions of them, racing one another from sky to earth. They splashed down upon everything, on the leaves and the ferns and the Stream. The birds skulked amongst the bushes trying to find shelter from them, for they did not like the raindrops, but the Stream spread his arms out wide, and loved to feel them falling upon him. He was so excited and happy, for he felt himself growing

40

stronger every hour, and he thought that when the Waterfall sent her children he would be quite strong enough to climb the hill. So he sang so gladly that he did not notice that the bell-birds had stopped calling.

Then on the third day of the rain, the Waterfall sent her children as she had promised. With white hair flying they came rushing down the valley, dashing and splashing as they ran. The birds heard them, and those who had begun to build their nests on the low trees flew about crying, "The floods, the floods!"

But the Stream did not notice the birds' terror. He had eyes only for that shouting, noisy crowd of white-haired Wavelets.

"Hurrah, hurrah," he shouted. "Now I shall soon be able to climb the hill. Here are my friends!" And he lifted his head and rushed to meet them.

On they came with tremendous force, and before the Stream knew what was going to happen, they had dashed into him, and were swirling and swishing, and driving him along before them.

They swirled so hard that the Stream felt quite giddy, and called, "Oh, not so quickly, not so quickly, wait a minute!"

But the Wavelets just laughed, and hurried on the harder, crying, "We can't wait. We're in a hurry to get to the hill."

The Stream had quite forgotten the hill in the shock, but at the Wavelets' words he remembered that they had come to help him climb it. So he said not another word about waiting, but hastened along with the others.

And in a very short time they came to the hill. There it stood, steep and straight, its gum-trees drenched with rain, and its bell-birds all silenced. But it held its head as proudly as ever up towards the sky, and took not the least notice of the Stream.

"Ah!" he cried, "soon you won't be so proud. Just wait till I run over your stiff head, then you'll have to look at me. Come on!" he shouted to the Wavelets, and then they were right at the foot of the hill.

"Is this the place?" cried the Wavelets.

"Yes," shrieked the Stream, "this is the hateful hill that won't get out of my way."

"Then get ready, we are going to push," cried the Wavelets, and the next moment the Stream felt a tremendous push behind, and he was lifted gradually above his banks up the side of the hill.

The pushing hurt him terribly, and took his breath away, but he did not mind. "Push harder!" he cried; "lift me higher."

Then the Wavelets gathered all their force and, running underneath the Stream, they pushed till below him he could see the trees on his banks, half covered by water, and just above him were the saplings on the hill. He felt he was rising, but still the top of the hill was a long, long way up, and he could never reach it at this rate. Already he felt weakened by the pain of being pushed so hard, but he would endure anything to gain his end.

So he called as loudly as he could, "Oh, can't you push any harder?"

"Yes," shrieked the Wavelets, and with one terrific effort they sent the Stream up, up, up, till he touched the trunk of the lowest sapling. Then just as he felt that at last he was going to have his wish, and run over the top of the hill, the Wavelets ceased pushing, weakened, and slipped from beneath him, and with a crash and a splash, the Stream fell back from the hill-side.

"Good-bye!" called the Wavelets, "we can't stay to help you any longer, we are going home. You must climb the hill by yourself," and off they ran down the valley.

But the Stream did not answer them. The shock of falling back from the hill-side had quite stunned him, and he lay still and silent between his banks.

By this time the rain had ceased falling, and now the sunbeams began to creep down through the clouds, and soon the trees were sparkling in the light, and the birds began to twitter and call to each other that the flood was over.

But though all the world was smiling, the Stream lay silently in the valley, taking no notice of the birds or trees or sunbeams, till at last he heard his name called, and looking up, saw the Lyre Bird standing beside him.

"I didn't expect to find you here," said the Lyre Bird. "I thought you would have been far over the hill by now. I saw the Waterfall's children come rushing down, and I heard the birds saying there was a flood, and that you were rising up the hill. How is it that you are still here?"

"Oh!" moaned the Stream, "don't remind me of it. The Wavelets were so rough. But here I am, and here I mean to stay."

"Do you mean that you don't want to go up the hill?" asked the Lyre Bird.

"Yes," said the Stream, "I shall be quite content in future to flow through the valley. I have found that hills are not meant for Streams to climb."

"You are quite right," agreed the Lyre Bird, "and I am so glad you have at last learned that. Now you will be contented and happy and sing as you go."

42

Then he called out to the other birds, "Listen, all of you. The Stream is no longer discontented. He has learned that water won't run up a hill, and he's going to be happy and gay in the valley."

"Hooray, hooray!" shouted the birds in chorus. Then they all began to sing—

"Flow along the valley,
　Little Stream so gay,
While the sunbeams golden
　Round about thee play.

"Hill-sides steep and barren
　Were not meant for thee;
Valley depths are better,
　All wise streams agree.

"Flow then, happy Streamlet,
　Singing every day,
Cheering with thy gladness,
　All things on thy way."

THE GALLANT GUM TREES

THE trees in the gully grew green and thick, for the stream that ran and danced all day over the rocks brought them nourishing food, which made them strong. The hot winds never blew on them, and the sun only sent his kindest rays upon them. So it came about that the Tree-ferns and Wattles, the Myrtles and Sassafras, which grew along the banks of the stream, were always cool and green and shady, and the most admired in the district.

Up on the hill-side where the young Gums grew, things were very different. The loose sandy soil in which their roots were embedded contained very little food for them, for all the water used to run down the hill to the stream in the gully. For this reason the Wattles and Myrtles got most of the Gum-trees' food as well as their own. But the Gums never grumbled. Of all the trees in the forest they were the bravest and most cheerful. When the hot winds blew and scorched their faces, they would laugh merrily together, and say: "No need of overcoats to-day!" When the cold wintry blasts came tearing down from the mountain, they would dance and wave their arms, shouting to each other, "Fine, fresh weather, isn't it? Makes one want to dance."

If the rain poured in torrents for days together they would gladly drink in all they could, saying: "There's nothing like a good shower bath for making you big and strong." And if the drought came and dried up all the moisture in the soil, so that there was scarcely any nourishment for them, they would hold up their heads and say—"We believe in fasting sometimes, it keeps us slim and graceful."

So, whatever the weather, the Gums were contented, and enjoyed their lives to the utmost. Because they were so happy everyone loved them, and the birds and bees would play amongst their leaves and make their homes in their branches; the native bears and opossums would climb their trunks, and feed on their leaves; and insects would hide under their bark for protection. The Gum trees loved them all and were glad to be of so much use in the world.

Indeed, there were very few things that they did not love, but the ones they cared for most of all were the green trees in the gully. They knew that everyone admired the gully-trees, but they were never hurt nor jealous; indeed they were as proud of the greenness and luxuriance of the gully-trees as if they themselves had made them.

"Look at those Tree-ferns," they would say, "did you ever see anything so cool and fresh?" Or they would ask—"Could there be anything more beautiful and graceful than those Wattles and Myrtles?"; and they would honestly wonder why the birds and bees ever came near them, when they could live amongst the trees in the gully. For they were quite unaware of their own charm and sweetness, and really believed that they were not worth looking at.

And the gully-trees agreed with them on that point. They were so used to being admired by everyone that they thought themselves the most beautiful things in the world, and even took it as a matter of course that the Gums should think so too. They were fond of the Gums, but in a very patronising way, and would laugh at them for being tall and scraggy instead of round and thick like themselves. The Gums laughed too, and so they were all good friends.

The gully-trees never thought of being grateful to the Gums for the shelter and protection they gave them from sun and wind, and the Gums never dreamed of being offended because the gully-trees took more than their own share of food.

They thus lived on quietly and contentedly for many years, watching the seasons come and go each with its own treasure. Then one day a very bad-tempered Summer arrived. She came very early, before Spring had left the land, and as she arrived in a fury, the gentler season fled before her. Scorching winds and blazing sunbeams followed in her train, and before many days were past the whole land was suffering from her cruelty. The smaller plants and flowers were shrivelled as though by a furnace; the young birds, unable to escape to cooler regions, dropped and died; even the big trees grew faint and weary, and bent their heads before her.

In the farms and orchards men went about with worried looks, for the young crops and fruit were being killed, and famine stared in their faces.

Down in the gully the trees moaned and sighed with pain, for they had never known such heat, and they cried to the Gums to try and shelter them. Up on the hill the heat was worst of all, and some of the younger Gums were beginning to moan, but their bigger brothers still talked cheerfully to each other, and tried to keep up the spirits of the weaker ones. When they heard the cries of the gully-trees, they were saddened, for it was beyond their power to protect them from the fiery blasts.

"Help us, oh, help us if you love us!" cried the gully-trees.

The Gums bent gently towards them and answered sadly, "We would give our lives to save you, you dear, beautiful things, but we are powerless."

The cruel Summer heard these words, and laughed mockingly.

"You would give your lives for them, would you?" she said with a sneer. "You will soon have a chance to do so." So saying, she raced away across the mountain.

That very night the chance came. The Sun went down a fiery ball behind the hills, and, as he disappeared, a red glow was seen to rise in the eastern sky.

"Is the Sun coming back again already?" asked a baby tree, in tears.

The bigger Gums shook their heads. "It is not the Sun," they said; "it is a greater enemy than he. It is the Fire."

At these words there rose from all the trees and bushes a wail of despair, for the Fire is the most dreaded of all enemies. Down in the gully the trees shook and trembled with terror.

"Is it coming this way?" they cried, for they could not see the red glow yet.

"It is coming this way, and coming quickly," answered the Gums gravely.

"Oh, what shall we do, what shall we do?" sobbed the gully-trees. "We shall all be killed!"

Their cries were drowned by a howl from the Summer winds, and at that instant the Fire appeared on the top of the opposite hill. With red hair flying and blue arms waving it leaped from tree to tree, licking up everything before it. Behind it came the hot winds, driving it forward and laughing fiendishly at their work.

Already the Gums on the hill-side could feel the breath of the flames, but though their faces were almost scorched, the sap ran cool and calm within them. Flocks of birds came screeching towards them, and flew rapidly past, together with a troop of bush animals, all crying aloud, "The Fire, the Fire!"

The gully-trees heard them, and wept piteously in their terror.

The sound of their friends' grief and terror roused a feeling in the heart of the Gums that they had never known before. It was their fighting instinct. Instantly they decided to fight to the death to save their darlings in the gully. They lifted their heads and waved their arms in defiance at the Fire, shouting in one voice—"Come and fight us if you dare!"

The Fire heard the challenge, and with a roar leaped right across the gully, over the gully-trees, and hurled its flames into the midst of the Gums. Fiercely the battle raged, the Gums dashing their green leaves into the face of the flames. But the Fire was stronger, and very soon the trees were overwhelmed and conquered. Then the Fire passed on, leaving the gully-trees all green and untouched; but on the hill-side stood a defeated army of burnt black trunks, where so short a time before the brave young Gums had dared the foe.

.   .   .   .

In a few days the Fire had burnt itself out, and then the Rain sent soft showers that cooled and refreshed the parched and burnt-up earth. After the rain had washed away all the black stains and dust, the gully-trees were as green and beautiful as they had ever been, and no one could tell by looking at them that they had so nearly perished in the flames. But the gully-trees themselves knew the danger they had escaped. They had no chance of forgetting their peril, for there before their eyes were the black trunks of the Gums which had saved them. And they did not laugh happily as of yore, but drooped their heads and mourned for their lost friends.

"It does not seem right that we should be as strong and healthy as ever, while our poor friends are all dead," said the Sassafras tree sadly.

"To think that we will never see their happy faces nodding to us again!" sighed the Wattle.

"Nor hear their merry voices calling to each other," said the Myrtle.

"Life will be very lonely without them," said the Tree-fern, "and I wish we had never laughed at them."

At this there was silence, for all the trees felt sad and ashamed to think that they had ever laughed at their brave friends on the hill-side.

The silence was broken by a tiny whisper which seemed to come from the ground, and which said—"Don't grieve, dear trees, we shall meet again."

The trees looked at each other in astonishment.

"What is it?" they asked each other. "It sounds like the voices of the Gum-trees."

"It is the spirit of the Gums," cried the Stream, who had heard all the conversation. "Listen, listen, and you will hear it again."

The trees all bent eagerly towards the ground, and again the soft voice spoke.

"We are not dead," it said, "though we are badly wounded. But our sap is still fresh and cool, and we will be ourselves again some day."

The trees could not keep still with excitement. Their leaves rustled and quivered with joy, and they asked, all together, "Oh, is it true, is it true?"

"Yes," called the Stream, as he danced along, "it is quite true. Before many seasons have passed your friends will be the same as ever. Fire cannot kill their brave hearts, and while a tree's heart is alive, it cannot die."

"Hurrah! hurrah!" shouted all the gully-trees, as they waved their arms with joy.

"Hurrah! hurrah!" cried the birds also, when they heard the cheering, and flew away to spread the news to the 'Possums and Native Bears.

And little by little the Gums began to recover and put forth little shoots to show that their wounds were healing. The kind rain sent showers which washed all the burnt leaves into the earth and gave the Gums fresh food, which strengthened them. When the Summer arrived again she was in a good temper and sorry for all the harm she had done; so she brought only gentle sunbeams and refreshing winds with her; and everything helped the Gums to recover.

At the end of a few seasons, all the earth had recovered from the fire. The flowers and small plants covered the ground more gaily than ever; the crops and fruit were bigger and more plentiful than they had ever been before, and on the hill-side the Gum-trees waved and sang quite merrily.

But a great change had come over them. Instead of the ragged, straggling things of dull green they had been before, there rose tier after tier of straight, strong trees, all thickly clothed with leaves of a glorious copper colour, which gleamed and glistened in the sunshine, and made the hill-side glow like burnished armour.

And no longer were the gully-trees the most admired, for everyone stopped to gaze at the hill-side and say: "Oh, what beautiful Gum-trees!"

The gully-trees themselves admired their friends more than anyone, and were never tired of telling them how lovely they were.

As for the Gums, they laughed and enjoyed life just in the same old way, and answered all the compliments by saying: "After all, it doesn't matter much what your face is like, if only your saps keeps cool and pure. Sap is the thing that counts!"

HOW THE FLOWER FAIRIES HELPED

THE Flower Fairies awoke from their winter sleep and began to look round. The sun was shining merrily and the soft breezes were playing chasings amongst the bushes. All round the birds were calling to each other cheerfully as they flitted from tree to tree. Everything was filled with life and joy, for it was spring.

"Hooray!" called one of the Fairies. "Winter is over at last. Wake from your sleep, O lazy ones, and greet the spring."

At her words, the Fairies began to collect in a group, dozens and dozens of them; from every bush and shrub they came dancing and laughing. When they were all gathered together they took hands, and danced in a ring, singing with loud, sweet voices:—

> "Wintry days have passed away,
>   Spring is here! Spring is here!
> Let us all be bright and gay,
>   Spring is here! Spring is here!
>
> "Birds are singing in the trees,
>   Spring is here! Spring is here!
> Sweet scents float upon the breeze,
>   Spring is here! Spring is here!
>
> "Flowers will soon be everywhere,
>   Spring is here! Spring is here!
> Blossoms beautiful and fair,
>   Spring is here! Spring is here!

When the song was finished, the Queen jumped upon a branch, and all the Fairies gathered round to hear what she was going to say. She waved her sceptre, which was a beautiful waratah, and when they were all near enough she spoke in a sweet, soft voice.

"Dear Fairies," she said, "I am very very glad to see you all together again, and I hope you are rested by your winter sleep, for I have important work for you this spring."

"We are ready to obey your commands," cried the Fairies in chorus.

The Queen smiled with pleasure. "You are all good children," she said, "and I know you will do your best to carry out my wishes. What I want is this. I want you not only to cover the earth with blossoms, but to go into the

They whispered in his ear, telling him all the beautiful secrets of fairyland

houses of mortals and into their hearts, and take your flowers with you, so that they may carry sweetness and happiness with them. I know it is not an easy task I am setting you, but it is well worth doing. And I shall be very proud of you all, if you can succeed."

Then a bright Fairy in a pretty pink dress stepped forward and said: "If it please your Majesty, I have a suggestion to make."

"We shall be very pleased to hear it, Boronia," said the Queen.

"I propose that we spread our flowers all over the land, not only in the bush, but in the gardens, that mortals are so fond of. Afterwards let us kill the garden flowers, and then the mortals will have to notice us."

"I don't think that would be very kind to the garden flowers," said the Queen. "We don't want to hurt them, for it isn't their fault that mortals prefer them to your blossoms. Can't someone suggest something else."

"I can," called a cross-looking Fairy in a very spiky dress. "I propose that we stick sharp spikes into mortals everytime they look at any flowers but ours." It was the Hakea, or Needlebush Fairy that spoke, and she had the reputation of being a cross-patch.

The Queen laughed at her words and said: "I don't think that would be a very good plan, Hakea, for it would make mortals hate instead of love us."

Just then a dainty little Fairy in a pale pink dress came shyly forward and said: "I suggest that we begin by making the children love us."

"That sounds much better, Bauera," said the Queen. "Have you any plan about beginning?"

"I think it would be a good idea to go into the schools and nurseries, and teach the young children to know and love us."

"That's a capital idea," cried the Wattle Fairy. "For if children know us when they are young they will never forget us."

"Yes, and when they grow up they will teach their children about us, and by-and-by everyone will know us quite well, and we will no longer be strangers in our own land." It was the Correa Fairy that spoke, and her voice was sad as she uttered the last words.

"You are a very clever child, Bauera, to think of such a plan," said the Queen, looking approvingly at the shy little Fairy, who blushed with pleasure at her words. "And now I think it would be wise to waste no time. Let us begin at once. I think it would be best for you all to look through the schools first, and come back in two days to tell me what you see. Then we can decide what to do next."

So the Fairies started off across the land in every direction and, as they passed, the earth beneath them bloomed forth in flowers of every shade and shape, till the ground was covered with a gorgeous carpet of red, yellow, white, pink, blue and green, while the air was filled with fragrance.

At the end of the second day, when the sunbeams were stealing home to their Father, the Sun, and the birds were singing their evening songs, the Flower Fairies met once more. Slowly they came across the earth from different directions but instead of laughing and singing as when they set out, they crept back quietly and silently. When they were all assembled the Queen gazed round at their sad faces, and asked: "Well, my children, what have you seen?"

The only answer was a burst of tears from the Epacris Fairy, who shook with sobs, but could not speak.

"Has no one seen anything?" asked the Queen anxiously. "Or what has happened to you all? Epacris, dear, don't cry. Tell me what you have seen."

Epacris dried her eyes, and turning to the Queen, said: "Oh, do not ask me what I have seen, it will only make you sad to hear."

"I am sorry for that," said the Queen, "but I must hear the truth."

"Then I shall tell your majesty. When we went off from here two days ago Eriostemon and I journeyed together. We went to a big school where there were hundreds of children, and we peeped through the window to see what they were doing. To our surprise, instead of reading from books, or doing sums, they were all busy drawing and painting flowers. I said to Eriostemon, 'This looks very hopeful,' and we both slipped into the room, and looked over the shoulder of the nearest child to see what flower he was drawing. It was a pansy. Then we looked on the next book. There was a poppy, then a fuchsia, then a rose, and

52

so on. Every child in that room was either drawing or painting a flower, but not one was copying an Australian flower."

The Queen looked very sad as she listened to the words of the Epacris Fairy. Then she looked round at the others, and asked, "But some of you must have better news than this?"

But the others all sadly shook their heads in silence. Only Hakea spoke, and she cried angrily: "The worst of it is, that those children were all quite satisfied to draw those foreign flowers."

"Not quite all," said the Bauera, gently. She had been the last Fairy to arrive, and had been too far at the back to speak before. But now she came to the front, and the others made way for her till she reached the Queen's side.

The Queen bent forward eagerly and asked: "Did you say 'Not quite all,' Bauera?"

"Yes," said Bauera, "I have found one child who is not satisfied to draw foreign flowers."

"Oh, do tell us about it!" cried all the Fairies together; and Bauera told her story.

"When I left here I went straight towards the city, for that is where most children live. I found my way to a school right in the heart of the town, where there were no trees or flowers of any kind. Here I found a lot of pale-faced children drawing flowers, and, like Epacris, I peeped over their shoulders to see what they were drawing. On every page was a foreign flower—at least, on every page but one, and it was bare, with not a single stroke upon it. Before it sat a boy, who looked different from the other children. His face was rounder and browner, and he looked more like the children we see in the bush. He was sitting with his pencil idle in his hand, and his big brown eyes were gazing out through the window at some swallows building their nest on the eaves.

"There was something in that boy's appearance that I liked, and I stayed for a few moments to watch him. While I was waiting there, the teacher came up, and asked to see his drawing. He was angry when he saw the empty page, and scolded the boy for being idle.

"Then the boy answered with words that filled me with joy. He said that he didn't want to draw poppies and carnations; that he never saw those flowers except in pictures, and he did not like them. He wanted to draw the flowers that grew in the bush by the creek at home, and his eyes filled with tears as he spoke.

"The teacher was very kind, and asked him gently what the flowers were like that grew by the creek at home, and the boy took his pencil, and in a few strokes drew two pictures on the paper. I bent over with curiosity to see what he had drawn, and there, to my delight, was a spray of my own flower and a piece of Correa!"

"Splendid, splendid!" cried the Fairies, while Bauera stopped for breath. "Do tell us the rest!" So Bauera continued:

"They were beautifully drawn, and I could see that the teacher was pleased with them, though he only said, as he pointed to my flowers: 'This is very like a small dogrose.'"

" 'That's what we called it at home,' said the boy, 'native dogrose.'"

"Then he drew several other flowers, Epacris, Tea-tree, and the Bottle-brush, and the teacher was very interested, and asked him how he remembered them so well. And the boy replied: 'Because I love them!'"

"Hooray, hooray!" shouted the Fairies, "he was a real Australian. Tell us what happened next!"

"Oh, just then a big bell rang, and the children all shut up their books, and school was over. Most of the children went off in twos and threes, but my boy was quite alone, and seemed to have no friends. I went with him to his home, which was a dull brick house in a dreary street, with not a tree or flower to be seen. So I did not wonder that he never saw foreign flowers except in books, for I guessed that he had come straight from the bush to this city house. I left him at the door, for I was afraid I should be late if I stayed longer. And that is all I have to tell."

"It is very well worth telling, Bauera," said the Queen, "and I am sure it has pleased us all to hear it. We were all very sad at what Epacris related, and I felt almost hopeless. But your story has quite cheered me, for while there is even one child who loves us there is hope for the others. Don't you agree with me?" she asked, turning to the other Fairies.

"We do, indeed," they answered in unison. Then the Wattle Fairy stepped forward, and spoke.

"I think," she said, "we should all unite in helping this boy, who is a true Australian. Let us never leave him, but watch over him, and fill his mind with the knowledge of beauty, so that he may be a great man and teach his fellows."

Then the other Fairies slipped away amongst the flowers, singing softly as they went.

How the Flower Fairies Helped

But Bauera jumped upon a moonbeam and floated away towards the city, on and on till she reached the dull brick house in the dreary street. She glided in through the open window to where the boy was lying asleep on his little bed, and bending over him, kissed his forehead, then glided out again. And the boy smiled with joy in his dreams.

The Fairies worked hard to help the boy. They never left him, and sleeping or waking there was always one of them at his side. They whispered in his ear, telling him all the beautiful secrets of fairyland; they touched his eyes with their finger-tips, and made him see the beauty that was all around him; and they kissed his hands so that he was able to draw the things that he saw.

Day by day the boy grew more like the Fairies, and his big brown eyes seemed to see more than the other children's eyes. The teacher noticed the difference in him, and was anxious to help him, so he brought big bunches of wild flowers to school and let the boy draw them instead of copying garden flowers. And the boy, because he loved the bush blossoms, painted them as no flowers had ever been painted before, and his work was shown to every visitor that came to the school.

But the boy did not care about the praise that was showered upon him. So long as he could paint his beloved flowers he was happy, and it did not matter to him whether other people admired his work or not.

And so the days passed into years; the boy left school, and was free to go out into the bush and gather the flowers for himself. The Fairies still were with him, showing him all the beauties to which most people's eyes are blind. And soon he knew every flower and blossom that grew—even the little humble plants that hide shyly away behind the others. And he had pretty names for them all. He would carry them home and paint them on paper, or china; while sometimes he would copy them in stone, carving them so gracefully that they looked as if they were really growing.

Thus his fame began to spread throughout the land; people came to see his work, and marvelled at its beauty; then they went away and told others, who also came to look. But the boy went on with his drawing and painting, regardless of them all.

Then one day a great artist came to visit Australia. His fame was known from pole to pole, and everywhere he was welcomed as the greatest artist in the world. He came to the town where the boy lived, and hearing of his work, said he would like to see it.

"It is not such work as you do," the people said, "but it is different to any we have here."

The great man smiled, and said he would be pleased to see the boy's work, and would not criticize him harshly.

So they took him to the room where the boy worked—just a little rough shed in the bush it was—and there they found the boy singing happily, for the Fairies were all around him.

The great man went slowly in, for he felt the presence of beauty, and the boy came forward to welcome him.

But the man's eyes went past the boy and rested on a carving on the wall. With a cry he went towards it, then stopped half-way to gaze at a newly-painted picture. From side to side he went in silence, looking at everything, while the people stood by, fearing that he was disappointed with the boy's work.

At last he turned to them and said, "This is genius."

And the news went forth amongst the people, and spread from land to land, till all the world heard that the great man had found a genius in Australia. Then people came from every land to greet the boy as one of the world's greatest artists.

But the boy, now grown to be a man, went on with his work, surrounded by the Fairies and unspoiled by all their praise. He was happy that his beloved flowers were becoming known to all men, as are the flowers of other lands. And when the people asked him where he found the beautiful blossoms that he painted and carved, he told them that they were the flowers of their own country.

"You tread them beneath your feet every day," he said. "You are too proud and blind to see them, and while you are gazing up and searching for rare things from far away, you are crushing and passing by the beauty at your feet."

So the people heeded his words and began to notice, and to love their own fair blossoms.

Out in the bush the Fairies met and danced and sang with joy. But the happiest of all was Bauera, for she had discovered the boy-artist.

THE CHRISTMAS BELLS AND THE HOLLY BUSH

THERE was one thing in the garden which the House Mother loved better than anything else, and that was the Holly Tree. She had brought it from England with her when it was a small plant in a pot, and she was quite a young girl. Now the Holly was a big tree and she was an old woman.

There were plenty of other trees and flowers in the garden, many of them far more beautiful than the Holly, but though the House Mother took great care of them all she gave extra attention and love to the Holly. If she had known what a very disagreeable tree it was, she never would have been so fond of it. But she saw in it all the beauty and happiness of her old home, and was blind to the fact that it was really a very proud, bad-tempered bush.

But though she was not aware of the Holly's faults, all the other flowers and trees in the garden were. They knew that it was the proudest and nastiest tree amongst them, and instead of being sweetened by the love the House Mother spent on it, it was only vain and arrogant. And it was so ungrateful that it would even prick her fingers if it noticed her paying attention to any other plant.

"You ought to be ashamed of yourself," said the Rose indignantly, when one day the Holly pricked the House Mother's finger so deeply that it bled. "How can you be so ungrateful?"

"Pooh!" said the Holly, "Why should I be grateful, I should like to know? She should be grateful to me for living in her garden."

"Oh!" exclaimed the Rose in horrified surprise. "Do you forget all that she has done for you all your life?"

"I don't see that she has done anything much, and she knows that I wouldn't stay here if she didn't please me."

"And what about the love she has always given you?"

"Oh, well, how can she help loving me when I am so beautiful?" And the Holly held his stiff head up higher than ever, and looked very ugly and conceited.

"How can she help loving you?" echoed the Rose, "I'll tell you how. Because you are vain and ungrateful and cruel, and do not deserve her love."

The Holly laughed affectedly as he answered—"The House Mother evidently doesn't agree with you. She sees that I am the most exquisite tree in her garden, and so of course she loves me."

"Not at all, not at all," said a Red Gum, that bent over the fence from the paddock outside. "The reason the House Mother loves you is not because you are beautiful, but because you remind her of her childhood and her old home, and the little cottage garden from which she brought you."

"What do you mean?" asked the Holly, indignantly turning towards the Red Gum. "I come from no cottage garden. I come from a noble line, and can trace my ancestors back for centuries."

"Perhaps so!" said the Red Gum, "but we are not speaking of your ancestors. I say that you came from a cottage garden, and your manners prove your want of breeding," and with that he waved back over the fence, and took no more notice of the Holly.

Instead of profiting by the Red Gum's remark, and making up his mind to improve his manners, the Holly grew ruder and crosser each day, till the other flowers almost hated him. He hadn't a nice word for anyone. He snubbed the little plants unmercifully and called them weeds and intruders; he was impudent to the big trees and called them upstarts; and the beautiful flowers, the roses, carnations, and stocks, he insulted most of all, for they were out in all their spring glory, and were admired and beloved by everyone.

Still the House Mother loved him and petted him, for even the wisest House Mothers cannot see into a tree's heart, and she did not know of the hatred and ill-feeling that was rife in her beautiful garden.

As the spring passed on into summer, the blossoms of the fairest flowers dropped and died one by one, till there wasn't a single bloom left on rose, carnation or stock. The Holly rejoiced to see the blossoms fade, for, as is the way with all jealous and discontented people, he could not bear to see beauty in anyone but himself. And when the last blooms died and disappeared, he became almost good tempered.

58

THE CHRISTMAS BELLS AND THE HOLLY BUSH

"Now," he said in a loud conceited voice, "I think you must all agree that I am the most beautiful thing in the garden. And when Christmas day comes, you will know that I am certainly the most important."

"Why should we know it especially on Christmas day?" asked a wild Clematis, who had only lately come to the garden, and did not know much about the garden flowers.

The Holly looked at her with pitying contempt. "Of course one must expect ignorance in such weeds as you, but as you ask me, I will tell you why I am most important on Christmas day. On that day all the flowers are dead, but I am in my full beauty, and people make songs about me, and pick great bunches of my scarlet berries to decorate their houses and churches."

"Your berries!" said the Clematis, "Where are they? I can only see dull green leaves on you."

The Holly looked at her disdainfully, but before he could think of what to say, there came a laugh from across the fence, and the Red Gum bent over.

"Ho, ho, friend Holly," he said. "So you are remembering the old world and the cottage garden now?"

"What do you mean?" demanded the Holly, who rather dreaded the Red Gum's satire.

"You were surely thinking of them just now when you explained to the Clematis why you were so important on Christmas day. For though that may be quite true of your family in the old world it is not at all the same here."

"Why is it not the same? Doesn't the House Mother pick a piece of me every Christmas to put on her plum-pudding?"

"Yes, but that is simply because she used to do so when she was a girl. We all know that the House Mother loves you, but we have never seen anyone else pick the red berries you speak of to decorate their houses."

The Holly looked foolish and uncomfortable at these words, but did not answer, for he knew that they were true.

"You live too much in the past, my friend," went on the Red Gum, "and you imagine that things are the same here as they were in your youth across the world. But they are not. At Christmas time in England when the snow is on the ground and all the other flowers are asleep, people are very glad to have your scarlet berries. But things are different in this land. There are plenty of flowers in bloom for Christmas day, and you have not a single berry on you. No one cares anything about you except a few old fashioned people like the House

Mother, whom you remind of their youth. All true Australians prefer their own Christmas flowers, and do not bother about you."

"What Christmas flowers have they?" asked the Holly, who had never been outside the garden and knew none of the bush blossoms.

"Christmas Bush and Christmas Bells, of course," replied the Red Gum.

"I never heard of them," said the Holly with contempt.

"Never heard of them?" echoed the Clematis; "why, I thought you were so clever that you knew everything. And you have never even heard of the beautiful Christmas Bush and Bells, which are far more lovely than you."

"Well, you will soon have a chance of seeing the Christmas Bells," said the Red Gum, "for there is a family of them growing beneath my shade, just outside the fence, and they will be in full bloom within the month."

The Red Gum's words were true. In a week the Christmas Bells began to come through the ground, first one little spear, then another, till in a short time there was a group of bright red bells waving in the breeze.

All the trees in the garden admired them, and soon grew to love them, for they were so bright and merry and full of fun. All except the Holly. He had to admit to himself that their red bells were far more beautiful than his own dull green leaves, but this only made him dislike them more than ever.

"Noisy vulgar upstarts!" he said with a sneer when the Bells rang cheerfully, and he never lost a chance to say something unkind about them. He was nastier to them than he had been to all the others put together, for he hated them worst of all.

The Christmas Bells could not understand him. They were loving, happy little flowers, with kind words for everyone, and at first they tried to make friends with the Holly. But he treated all their advances so cruelly, that they were hurt, and did not dare to approach him. And their pretty heads hung sadly when they heard his unkind remarks about them. Still they never returned his nastiness, and never spoke an unkind word about him.

As the end of the year drew near the weather grew hotter and hotter. A furious blast of scorching wind blew from the west, drying up everything on its way. The tender leaves of the garden plants shrivelled and died, and the plants themselves began to droop and pine away. The Holly felt it most of all. It was the hottest summer he had ever known in his life, and he longed for the snow and cold wind of his youth. The House Mother did all she could for him, but water was scarce, and she could spare very little. Each day he grew fainter. He did not take it quietly as did the other flowers, but grumbled the whole day long, and by his bad temper exhausted what strength he had left, so that when Christmas Eve arrived he was really very ill and weak.

"I wish I had never come to this hateful country," he cried. "It is not fit for decent trees to live in."

"It's quite fit for the trees that belong to it," answered the Red Gum, who was not troubled by the heat.

"Oh, of course it's good enough for coarse uncultured things like you," retorted the Holly.

"It's a pity you came here," replied the Red Gum.

"Yes, it is," wailed the Holly, and he began to moan miserably.

"Oh, don't be unkind to him, Red Gum!" cried the Christmas Bells, the only flowers left alive.

"He deserves it," grumbled the Red Gum. "He has always run down our land."

"Yes, but he is ill now."

"I don't care. I hope the wind will kill him," said the Red Gum savagely.

"Oh, Red Gum, Red Gum," cried the Bells, "we are shocked at you."

"Well, I don't exactly hope it will kill him, but I hope it will teach him a lesson," admitted the Red Gum.

Here they were interrupted by a deep moan from the Holly, who was now past speech. He looked so weak and pitiful that the Red Gum's heart softened towards him, and when the Bells cried, "Oh. Red Gum, lend him your shade, that will help him!" he did not answer, but bent across the fence, and threw his shadow over the Holly, protecting him from the sun.

The Holly opened his eyes and looked up, and the Bells and Red Gum saw something in his glance that had never been there before. It was a look of gratitude.

Instantly the Christmas Bells forgot the past. All they thought of was that here was a fellow plant dying for want of help. They put their heads together, and asked—"What can we do? What can we do? We must save him."

"Nothing can save him now but the Storm Fairy," said the Red Gum.

"Where is the Storm Fairy?" asked the Bells in one voice.

"Miles away, down by the sea."

"Couldn't you call to him to come?"

"He wouldn't hear me."

"Would he hear if we all rang our loudest?" asked the biggest Christmas Bell.

"Yes, he might hear that," said the Red Gum.

"Then do let us try!" called the Bells.

And they began to ring. "Ding-a-ding, ding-a-ding, ding, ding, ding!" they went, growing louder at each peal. Their music travelled above the noise of the Westerly Wind, across the plains, through the bush, over the mountains, to the coast, till at last it reached the sea where the Storm Fairy was.

The Storm Fairy heard it, and wondered what it was. As it grew more and more persistent, he determined to go and find out. So he started off towards it. Across the mountains he went, through the bush, till he came to the plains. The farther he travelled the louder the ringing grew, and at last he realized that it was someone ringing for help.

"I suppose that Westerly Wind has been up to his games again," he said to himself. "I must hurry along and prevent him doing too much mischief."

So he hurried onwards with a rush and a roar towards the garden.

The Red Gum saw him in the distance, and told the Bells.

"Don't stop ringing," he said, for they were growing very tired. "Don't stop, or he may pass by and not know we need him."

So the Bells swung themselves backwards and forwards with a fresh effort, although they were now so tired they could scarcely move. But they glanced at the drooping Holly, and determined to do their utmost.

The Storm Fairy stopped in the distance to listen; heard the fresh effort of the Christmas Bells; found where it came from and started off towards it. With a rush and a roar he came, accompanied by a train of black clouds. Half way across the plain, he met the Westerly Wind.

"I will teach you to behave!" he cried, and hurled a thunderbolt at him.

62

THE CHRISTMAS BELLS AND THE HOLLY BUSH

The Westerly Wind did not wait to fight, but turned and fled far away across the land. And the Storm Fairy went on his way.

"I'm coming, I'm coming," he shouted as the Bells sent out a fresh peal, and the next minute he had reached them.

He saw at a glance what had happened; saw the shrivelled garden, and the insensible Holly in the centre; and he saw the Christmas Bells outside the fence, now still and exhausted after their exertion.

"That Westerly Wind has been having a fine game," he said. "It looks as if I were only just in time. But I can save you all."

He gave a loud shout which shook the sky, and immediately the rain began to fall. Down it came, first in drops, then thicker and thicker, till the whole country was hidden in a sheet of falling water. All through the night it fell, soaking into the parched earth, and bringing fresh life to the plants. One by one they revived and lifted their heads, and stretched out their arms to drink in all they could.

When the morning came the Storm Fairy had passed on, but he had left a soft, cool, moist breeze behind him, and the garden rejoiced.

Before the sun was up very high, the House Mother came out to see how her dear plants were. With her came her little grand-daughter, who clapped her hands and ran about from plant to plant, wishing them all a merry Christmas. For it was Christmas day.

"I must pick a piece of Holly for the pudding," said the Home Mother, going towards her favourite.

But the little girl had caught sight of the Christmas Bells outside, and ran towards them crying, "Oh, here are some lovely Christmas Bells. Let us have them for the pudding, Granny."

The House Mother looked over the fence, and saw the red Bells swinging happily to and fro, without a trace of the hard work they had done the day before.

"They are very beautiful," she said, "and perhaps we should have them. As this is your first Christmas with me, dear, and you are a little Australian, we shall have a real Australian Christmas," and with these words she walked away from the Holly, and over to where the Christmas Bells were growing.

The other plants all looked at the Holly, expecting to see him very angry. But instead, to their surprise, a sweet smile was on his face, and he nodded pleasantly towards them.

"She is quite right," he said. "The Christmas Bells are the best and bravest of us all, and they deserve the place of honour. I know I have been vain and unbearable to you all, and most unkind to them, but they have taught me many things by their forgiveness, and I am glad that they are to take my place to-day, and I am proud to call them cousins!"

"Hurrah!" cried the Red Gum, as the Holly finished speaking. "That's the way for an English tree to talk, and I am proud to call you cousin," and he leaned down over the fence and gave the Holly a friendly kiss.

And the Christmas Bells rang with happiness, for by their love they had brought peace and goodwill into the garden.

THE WAVE

OUT on the depths of the deep blue ocean a Wind went wandering. He crept gently over the sleeping water, scarcely disturbing it as he passed. He was looking for some Waves to play with, but there were none to be found. The ocean's face was as smooth as a millpond, without one ripple to break its surface. The first rays of the rising sun stole up over the rim of the distance, but still the Waves slept on.

"Lazy things," said the Wind to himself. "I think I'll wake them."

So he puffed out his cheeks as far as he could, and, choosing a spot where the sea was bluest, he blew with all his might.

Instantly a dozen tiny Waves sprang up, wide awake.

"What are you doing?" they asked, crossly.

"Come and play," said the Wind.

"No, it's too early. We're going to sleep," and they turned slowly over and went to sleep again.

All except one little Wave. She had never seen the Wind before; for, indeed, she had only just been blown into life. Before the Wind had breathed upon her, she had been sleeping peacefully beneath the ocean, and had never been to the top; but now she had come right to the surface into the fresh air, and she wanted to stay there. So she did not lie down again with the others, but stayed and looked at the Wind.

She saw that he looked disappointed when the others turned over and went to sleep again, and she was such a gentle, happy little Wave that she did not like to disappoint anyone. So she said, shyly, to the Wind: "I'll play with you if you like."

The Wind looked at her for a moment, thinking how small she was. Then he said: "You are a very tiny Wave, but I believe I can soon make you big enough to play with."

So he blew upon the Wave, at first gently, and then gradually with more force, until he had lifted her high up from the surface, and she was quite a large Wave.

The Wind looked at her with approval, for, indeed, she was a Wave to admire.

65

She was all of a bright sea-green, with a tinge of blue, which broke into a crest of snow-white foam as she raised her head.

"I think you are big enough now to play with," said the Wind, "and I am quite sure you are pretty enough."

The Wave smiled with delight, and curled over with a joyful gurgle. "Come on, then; come and catch me," she called, and in a moment she was racing over the ocean with the Wind behind her.

"Oh, this is joy!" cried the Wave, as she felt the Wind behind her blowing her forward, ever forward. "To think that I should have been sleeping at the bottom of the ocean all this time, when I might have been playing here! Dear Wind, how can I thank you for waking me?"

"Don't try," said the Wind. "Just play with me, and I shall be satisfied."

So on across the ocean's face they went, chasing and catching, jumping and falling, while the Wave danced and bubbled with joy.

The sunbeams saw them, and came to join the fun, and they darted through the Wave, flashing and sparkling as they moved.

"Oh, you pretty things," cried the Wave, jumping up to catch them. They never rested for a moment, but darted backwards and forwards, laughing all the time.

She was such a young and happy Wave that it was no wonder that everyone wanted to play with her. The little fishes came up to the surface, and swam through her, leaving a tiny ripple behind them as they passed. The sunbeams saw the fishes, and darted after them, and the Wave laughed with glee at the sight.

Then a beautiful white bird came sailing along, and he sank down gently on to the Wave.

"Oh, you beauty!" she said, as she rocked him gently to and fro. The bird was so contented that he wanted the Wave to stay and nurse him all day.

But the Wind was growing impatient, and cried out:

"Come along, little Wave. There are many things to be seen, and we must make haste."

So the Wave said good-bye to the white bird, and danced off with the Wind.

As they travelled along they met many more birds and fishes, and the sunbeams went with them all the time, brightening the heart of the Wave, till she felt so happy that she thought there could be nobody in the whole world so glad as she.

66

And she thought that the whole world was made up of birds and breeze and sunbeams and little fishes.

She was soon to learn that there were other things than these in the world.

Above the voices of the sea-birds there came a new sound, strange to the ears of the Wave. "Swish-swish, swish-swish," it came across the water, and the Wave stayed still to listen.

"What is it?" she asked.

"A boat," replied the Wind.

"What is a boat?"

"The thing that Humans use to come upon the sea."

"I want to see it," said the Wave.

"Well, come and I'll show it to you."

The Wind helped her along, and they travelled so quickly that the little fishes were left behind. But the Wave was too excited to notice that. She was most curious to see this new thing, which the Wind called "a boat." As she moved along she could hear the "swish-swish" growing louder and louder, till at last she could hear nothing else.

"Look now," cried the Wind, and lifting her head the Wave saw a large white boat coming towards her. It had four long white feelers, two on each side, which moved rapidly all together, dipping in and out of the sea all the time. It was these things which made the "swish-swish." It looked like a great big animal with four long legs, and the Wave felt frightened, for she had never seen anything so big before. She thought she would run away, but before she had time to move, the nose of the boat was right up beside her. It did not hurt her, but gave her just a sharp push that tickled her and made her laugh aloud. She was just curling round to feel it again, when she heard a voice say: "Oh, what a darling Wave!"

She looked up quickly, and there, leaning over the edge of the boat, was the prettiest sight she had ever seen. Three children were looking down at her, with their heads close together, their bright curls dancing in the breeze, and their faces shining with delight. They clapped their hands, and she tried to jump up to catch them. But she was not big enough to reach the top of the boat, so she danced along beside it.

"That's the prettiest Wave I've ever seen," said one child.

"Oh, I like the ones on the beach best," said another.

67

Indeed she was a wave to admire

THE WAVE

"Yes, the waves at Bondi are the prettiest in the world," said the third. Then they went on to talk of how the waves broke up on the beach at Bondi and washed round their feet when they paddled, and rolled them over on the sand when they bathed, and they all agreed that Bondi was the most beautiful place in the world, and they wished they could go back there.

The Wave listened to all they said, and she longed to see this wonderful Bondi of which they spoke, where the waves rolled the children over on the beach. She had enjoyed playing with the fishes and the birds, but now that she had seen these pretty pink and white children she had lost interest in her first playmates, and only wanted to play with children."

"Where do these children come from?" she asked the Wind.

"From that land over there," said the Wind.

She looked to where he was pointing, and saw, for the first time, a distant shore with green hills sloping down to the sea.

"Is that Bondi?" she asked eagerly.

"Oh, no; Bondi is a long way from here."

"How do you get there?"

"You must travel on and on for miles and miles. It is right across the ocean," replied the Wind.

"Have you ever been there?"

"Oh, yes; often."

"Did you like it?"

"Yes; I think it is one of the most beautiful places in the world. And I have such fun there, blowing the people's hats off and puffing their hair into their eyes. There are lovely waves there, too, and the children swim in them. Would you like to go there?"

"Oh, yes, yes," cried the Wave. "Could you take me?"

"Yes, if you would not grow tired on the way."

"Oh, no; I will not tire. Do take me, dear, dear Wind."

"Very well," said the Wind. "Let us start at once."

So off they went.

The Wind puffed out his cheeks till they looked as if they would burst, and blew upon the Wave to help her along. She lifted her foam-crowned head into the air, and raced along before him. Over the ocean they went at such a rate that even the sunbeams could scarcely keep up with them. Some wild sea eagles saw them and came rushing along to look, shouting "Go on, Wave, you'll win," for they thought it was a race. A crowd of porpoises heard the sea eagles, and also began to applaud, waving their fins wildly in the air as they rolled over. They looked so funny that the Wave could hardly run for laughing.

"Wait a minute, Wind," she cried, and she stopped running, and gurgled slowly past the fat porpoises, tickling them as they passed.

Then on they went again, rushing and tearing. They passed many things on the way that the Wave had never seen before, although they were all old friends to the Wind. Big steamers came ploughing up the sea, frightening the Wave at first, till she found it was fun to slap up against them; big ships with white sails came gliding over the water, and she liked them better, and stayed to play around their bows, while the Wind whistled through their sails.

But the ships and steamers passed upon their way, and so the Wind and the Wave went travelling on again. Once they passed a boat like the one the children had been in, and the Wave danced up to look if there were any children there. But all she saw were two brown-faced fishermen, so she hurried past.

At last they came to an island, and as the Wave had never been close to land, they went to look at it. There were rough rocks all along the sea's edge, and a couple of men fishing.

"Where is the beach? Where are the children?" asked the Wave.

"There is no beach here, and no children—only grown-up men."

"Then we won't wait," said the Wave, "for I do not like the look of those rough rocks."

"You are right. Those rocks are rough, and would tear you to pieces if you went too near them."

"Then let us hurry past them," said the Wave; so they ran as hard as they could till the island and the rocks were left far behind.

But although they saw so many things that were new and strange, the Wave was not much interested in them. All she could think of was the long white beach at Bondi where she could roll the children over in her arms. Only that morning she had never heard of a beach or of children and she had been perfectly happy and contented; but now she knew that nothing would satisfy her but that beautiful beach of which those three children had talked.

"Is it very far now?" she asked the Wind, as the sun was beginning to travel down the western sky.

THE WAVE

"No," replied the Wind. "We shall soon be there now."

They journeyed on again in silence for a little while; then the Wind said:

"Do you see that dark line at the edge of the sea?"

The Wave lifted her head, and looked across the water to where a long blue line rose into the air.

"Yes, I see it," she said.

"That is Australia, and Bondi is straight before us. If we hurry we shall get there before sunset."

The Wave bubbled with excitement. "Sing to me, dear Wind," she said. So the Wind sang, and she danced along before him.

As they drew nearer, the blue line became more and more distinct, and they could see trees and cliffs, and long white lines between the cliffs.

"Those are the beaches," said the Wind, "and that long one with the low ground behind it is Bondi."

The Wave danced more quickly than ever.

"Oh, come on," she cried. "I can see children," and on they went.

The beach was quite near now, and they could see men and women walking along, and at the water's edge ever so many children playing, and the Wave saw that there were many other Waves now, all running up to the beach.

"Oh, the beautiful beach and the dear children!" she cried. "If only I can hold those children in my arms, and kiss that beach, I shall die happy. Help me, good Wind."

Then the Wind puffed out his cheeks wider than ever, and, bending low behind the Wave, blew hard and lifted her high. With arms outstretched and foam-hair flying, she raced along before him. In a minute she had reached the other Waves, all running to the shore but she ran fastest of all. Higher and higher the Wind lifted her, and she felt herself growing stronger. The weight of water below and behind seemed to be urging her forward; just in front she could see a group of children paddling, and behind them lay the beautiful shining white sand. She stretched out her arms still wider, lifted her head still higher, and with one leap reached the shore. Straight up she stood in a clear green wall, with a crest of white foam. For a second she seemed to stand still, then she hurled herself forward upon the group of children. Laughing and screaming, they tumbled along the sand beneath her, as she rolled them over with her arms. She wanted to wait and play with them, but she was moving too quickly to stop.

On she went, up the white beach. Her heart was aching with joy. Tenderly and softly she kissed the sand as she passed, but each kiss seemed to leave her weaker, and as she reached the highest watermark the joy of lying on the dear beach was too much for her, and her heart broke.

Then slowly and gently the mother sea drew her back down the beach, till she was lost again in the deep blue ocean. And the Wind sighed sadly for the loss of his dear little companion, who had only lived for one short day.

The FLOWER FAIRIES

IT was a hot sunny day in October. Early in the morning Dickie's sisters had sent him out into the bush to get flowers to decorate the house; but, though he had been out a long while, and walked a long way, he had only gathered a few. For he had spent his time looking for flannel flowers, and they were very scarce.

The few flowers he had in his hand looked as flowers generally do look when they have been picked by little boys. Some of them had scarcely any stalk at all, and most of them had been pulled up by the roots; so altogether it was not a very pretty bunch.

Dickie could see this for himself, and he also knew that his sisters would be very disappointed if he did not take home anything better.

"Someone must have pulled all the flannel flowers," he grumbled to himself as he walked along. This was quite true, but he did not stop to think that it was because other people had pulled the flowers up by the roots, just as he himself had done, that there were no flannel flowers left. So he went on looking all round and searching under ferns and shrubs for the flowers he wanted.

After a time he came to a little gully, where beneath the tall gums clumps of white flannel flowers waved amongst the grey rocks.

"Oh, what beauties!" Dickie exclaimed as he saw them, and he at once began to pick them as fast as he could, tearing them up roots and all in his hurry. At last he had gathered every single one of the pretty flowers, and then he sat down to arrange them in his bunch.

It was cool and quiet in the shade, and he was very tired, so he thought he would just lie down on the ferns for a while before he set out for home. He lay flat on his back, gazing up at the blue sky through the trees. The gently waving boughs of the wattles and the gum trees above his head made him feel drowsy, and he was just dozing off to sleep when suddenly he was aroused by the sound of someone crying very softly.

He sat up quickly and looked round. There, sitting beside his bunch of flowers was the daintiest, prettiest little fairy a boy had ever seen. She wore a white frock edged with green, and on her yellow hair was a little green cap. In her hands she held some of the flannel flowers from Dickie's bunch, and she was weeping bitterly.

Dickie sat and stared at her. He had often read about fairies, but had never seen a real live one before. He had always thought they were happy joyful beings, and was surprised to see this one crying like an ordinary little girl.

The fairy did not see him, but kept on weeping and weeping, and every now and then she kissed the flowers, and said softly "Poor things, poor things!"

Now, Dickie was really a nice little boy, and he did not like to see girls crying, so at last he said, "What's the matter, little fairy? Don't cry."

The fairy looked up quickly, and Dickie said again—

"Who are you? What's the matter. What are you crying for?"

"I am the fairy of the flannel flowers, and I am grieving for these poor flowers," said the fairy sadly.

"Why, what's wrong with them?" asked Dickie in surprise. "They're beauties."

"Yes, they were very beautiful, but now they're all dead. Some cruel being has pulled them out by the roots, and killed them."

At this Dickie looked a little bit ashamed, though he did think it silly to make so much fuss over a few flowers. The fairy saw the look, and said in a sharp voice, "Was it you who picked them?"

"Yes," said Dickie. Then as the fairy looked very angry, he added quickly: "they are for my sister to decorate with. I must take them home now."

"No," answered the fairy. "You must come with me."

"I can't," said Dickie, "I must go home."

"You must come with me," repeated the fairy.

"I won't!" cried Dickie, and he snatched up his flowers and began to run.

"Stop him," cried the fairy in a loud voice, and in an instant Dickie felt his feet caught fast by the bracken. He fell flat on his face, while the ferns put out dozens of arms and held him so fast, that he could not move.

74

THE FLOWER FAIRIES

"Now carry him to the Queen," said the fairy, and as soon as she spoke, the wattle tree above him stretched down a long arm, and picked him up into the air. For a second the wattle held him, then tossed him across to the next tree; then he was tossed to the next and the next, till he was quite out of breath. At last a tree fern caught him and held him tight. Then, very gently, so as not to hurt the young fronds, the tree fern rolled him down into the heart of his leaves. It seemed to Dick that, as he rolled, he grew smaller and smaller, until at last, when he reached the bottom, he was only as big as the fairy.

It was just as well he had grown small, for if he had stayed big there would have been no room for him, because the heart of the tree fern was crowded with fairies. As Dick rolled in, they all looked at him, and he heard a voice say, "Here he is."

It was the fairy of the flannel flowers who had spoken. She was seated on a curled-up fern-frond, beside another larger fairy who was dressed in deep red with a crown on her head, which looked to Dick like a waratah. All round her was seated other fairies in different coloured dresses. Some wore frilly gowns of white velvet, and others were dressed in yellow satin, while some wore soft pink silk, or blue gauze, and many other kinds of dresses. It seemed to Dickie that he knew them by sight, as indeed he did really, for they were the fairies of all the bush flowers, buttercups in yellow satin, boronia in pink silk, and many others that Dickie had often picked in the bush.

They sat round on the fronds of the tree fern, and as the Flannel Flower fairy spoke they all looked very hard at Dickie.

They were so small that Dick did not feel frightened of them at first, but suddenly he remembered that he also was very small now, and then he began to look round to see if he could get out. But every leaf of the tree fern was guarded by a fairy, and there was no way of getting past. So he just stayed where he was and waited.

"This is the boy who killed my flowers," said the flannel flower fairy to the Queen.

The Queen bent down and looked at Dick, then asked sternly—

"Why did you kill the flannel flowers?"

"I didn't kill them," said Dickie.

"O-o-oh!" said all the flower fairies together, and the white-robed fairy said, "Why, see, he still has them in his hand."

Dickie looked down, and there was his bunch of flowers still in his hand.

"I picked them for my sisters," he said, "but I did not mean to kill them."

"Then why did you pull them up by the roots?" asked the Queen.

"I did not know it would kill them," said Dickie, beginning to cry, for all the fairies looked so stern and sad, that he felt quite miserable.

"I wanted a nice bunch, and I picked them quickly, and their roots came up, but I didn't know flowers could fe-e-el," and here he began to cry just as badly as the flannel flower fairy had cried.

"Little boys that don't know must be taught," said the Queen. "You must learn that flowers do feel. We live to make human beings happy, and are pleased when they pick our blossoms to keep in water and brighten their rooms. But every time you pull a flower out by the roots, that flower dies, and all its children die, and no more grow from it. And if everyone pulled up the roots there would soon be no flowers left, and the world would be a very dreary place to live in."

"I do not think," the Queen went on, "that you are a wicked boy; you are just thoughtless. But you must be taught to think of other people's feelings. Now you will learn what a flower feels like when it is pulled out by the roots."

Then she turned to the fairies, and said "Teach him his lesson."

Instantly a spiky Wattle fairy flew towards him and tweaked a hair out of his head.

It hurt very much, and Dick cried out, "Stop it!" but before he could move another fairy came, and then another, and another, and each one tweaked a hair out of his head, and each hair hurt worse than the last, till he could stand no more, and he called out to the Queen, "Oh, make them stop. Please make them stop. I'll never pull another flower up by the roots. Do make them stop."

"That will do," said the Queen, "I think he has learned his lesson," and all the fairies flew back to their places.

Then the Queen turned to Dick and said kindly, "I think you will always remember now to be kind to all living things, even if they are only flowers."

"Yes, I will," promised Dickie, and he meant it.

"Now take him back," said the Queen, and the tree fern took hold of him, and began to roll him up again.

"Good-bye," he called, as he neared the top, and all the flower fairies answered, "Good-bye, good-bye," and just as he reached the edge, the flannel flower fairy flew after him, and pushed a big bunch of beautiful white blossoms into his hand.

"Take these," she whispered, "they will help you to remember."

The flower fairy was weeping like an ordinary little girl

He took the flowers, and the next moment was being tossed back by the tree branches, until he reached the wattle which had first lifted him up.

In a minute he was lying amongst the ferns again, with no sign of a fairy anywhere. But there was the bunch of flannel flowers to remind him of his promise to the Queen, so he knew it could not have been just a dream.

THE PROPER WAY

THE young Dottrel wanted to build a nest, but did not know how to begin. He had been in the world just a year, and had spent most of his time running about the sand, catching little crabs and worms and other things good to eat. But now that the Spring had come, and all the other birds were making nests, he felt that he would like to build a home for himself and his little wife; and as he did not know how to begin, he looked round for someone who could tell him.

Behind him, amongst the trees in the bush, he could hear many birds talking and calling to each other, as they flew about collecting material for their new homes. The Dottrel did not know any of the bush birds, but as they sounded so friendly and happy, he thought they would not mind giving him a little information. So he ran across the sand and through the grass at the edge of the lagoon where he lived, and entered the bush.

Here he found hundreds of birds, of all sizes and colours, flying busily about. They took no notice of him as he ran along the ground towards them, but, as they did not seem unfriendly, he was not very shy. He looked round to see which bird he should speak to first, but, before he could open his beak to address anyone, he heard a voice behind him say: "Hullo, my young friend! What are you doing here?"

The Dottrel turned to look at the speaker, and found it was the Red-bill, a bird he knew quite well by sight, for he lived in the reeds on the edge of the swamp. He was quite pleased to see a familiar face, and said: "I have come to ask how to build a nest."

"How to build a nest?" repeated the Red-bill. "Why, that's quite easy. You just get a few reeds and twist them round and fix them in a clump of grass, and your nest is built."

"It sounds easy," said the Dottrel, "but where do you get the reeds?"

"Oh, break them off, or pull them up with your beak."

The Dottrel looked at the Red-bill's big, strong beak, and, thinking of his own, which was slim and slender, he replied doubtfully—"I am afraid my beak is not strong enough to break reeds."

"No, it doesn't look fit for much," agreed the Red-bill. "Why don't you make it grow?"

"Is that the only way to build a nest?" asked the Dottrel, ignoring the Red-bill's question.

"The only proper way," replied the other with dignity, as he stalked away.

"What's that I hear?" asked a small bird with a long, sharp beak, that came swiftly darting towards the Dottrel at that moment. "What did Red-bill say was the only proper way?"

"He said that the only proper way to build a nest was to break off reeds and twist them in and out."

"Twisted reeds!" said the other scornfully, "why, whoever wants to build a nest of reeds?"

"I don't," said the Dottrel.

80

THE PROPER WAY

"I should think not," said the other, who was a Honey-eater. "No sensible bird does. The right way to make a nest is to get little roots and fibres, and threads of plants, and weave them into a basket hanging on two twigs."

"That sounds very pretty," said the Dottrel admiringly, "but the grasses which grow on the sand where I live are so stiff that I don't think they would twist into a basket."

"You should look for other grass then," said the Honey-eater, "for that is certainly the best way to build a nest. It is so cosy, and when the wind blows it is like being in a swing."

"Don't you take any notice of what he says," interrupted a tiny green bird with a red head, who had come up unnoticed. "Don't you build a nest like his, or you will rock right out when the wind blows. You build a long nest like mine where you can sit deep down at the bottom, and nothing can turn you out."

The speaker was the Redhead, and he was so fussy and self-important that the Dottrel was quite impressed.

"That certainly sounds safer," he agreed.

"Of course it is," said the Redhead. "Why, there isn't a nest in the bush as safe as mine!"

"Your nest safe?" exclaimed a Jacky Winter, who had flown up to hear what was being said. "Why there isn't a nest in the bush that's easier to see. Even the smallest boy can see it. The proper way to build a nest," he added, turning to the Dottrel, "is to make a tiny little cup of a nest on the fork of a branch. Then no one will see it, for it is too small!"

"Yes, that ought to be safe," said the Dottrel admiringly, "for I can understand that a boy would not easily see a nest as small as that."

"No, but he would see your tail sticking over the edge," cried a Native Canary, who had joined the group.

The Dottrel looked worried, as he said: "Of course, if a nest were too small, there wouldn't be much room to sit."

"Of course there wouldn't," agreed the Native Canary. "And it is silly to have a nest that your head and tail stick out of. Now, the proper way to make a nest is to cover it all over, with just a hole in the side where you can slip in and out without being seen."

"What a horrible, stuffy idea!" cried a Fantail. "It's quite hot enough as it is, without burying oneself in a nest like that. The way I build a nest is like this. I make it round and open, with a chimney underneath to keep me cool," and she fanned herself with her outspread tail, exclaiming, "How hot it is!"

The Dottrel looked at her with admiration. "I would like a house with a chimney underneath," he said. "Of what do you make it?"

"Cobweb and stuff. Cobweb makes such a nice soft covering, just like kid."

"Yes," broke in a little Tree-runner sarcastically, "and as all boys know that kid grows on trees, they, of course, never think it is a nest. The proper way to make a nest is to put it in the fork of a branch, and cover it with the bark of the tree. Then anyone who sees it, thinks it is just part of the branch, and walks past."

"I really don't see why you small birds spend so much time in finishing off the outside of your nests," cried a Magpie. "So long as the inside is soft and comfortable, who cares what the outside is like? I build my nest in the quickest way I can, with twigs and sticks, and if people do see, I don't care, for I place it too high for them to reach it. Don't you waste your time finishing off the outside," he said, turning to the Dottrel. "I never do."

"Oh, we all know that!" interjected the Peewee. "We all know that you are too untidy to finish off, and you have rough sticks jutting out all over your nest. It's a marvel that your children don't get killed on them when they are trying to leave home. Now the proper way to build a nest is to make it a nice tidy round mud basin. You can easily get the mud anywhere, and there is no need then to fly about all over the country looking for suitable sticks."

"Ha, ha, ha!" laughed the Kookaburra, "it seems to me it wastes as much time carrying mud as sticks." He turned towards the Dottrel as he spoke, and lowering his voice, said confidentially, "Don't you carry the mud. Let the ants do it for you."

"Ants!" repeated the Dottrel in surprise. "What have they to do with it?"

"The White Ants build a big earth nest in a tree, and I go and use it."

"But what becomes of the ants?"

"I eat them!" said the Kookaburra, bursting out laughing.

"Oh! how cruel!"

"It's fun catching them."

"Ugh! I don't like ants, and I couldn't live amongst them, so I don't think I'll make a nest like yours, Mister Kookaburra."

"All the more ants for me, then!" laughed the Kookaburra, as he flew away

"Why bother about having mud on a tree at all?" asked a Bee-eater, a gorgeously-coloured bird with long tail feathers. "The proper place for mud is on the ground, and that's the best place for a nest. If you take my advice, you will not spend your strength in carrying mud up a tree, but you will dig a hole in a bank of earth, and leave your eggs there."

As he spoke a large ugly bird stalked up, and said: "I think there is something very cowardly in hiding your eggs away in a hole like that. No one can accuse me of being a coward. I build a high mound of leaves and earth and leave my eggs there."

"That's very brave of you," said the Bee-eater, "and it's very kind too. For it must be so convenient for people to find."

"Not at all," said the Brush Turkey, for that was the big bird's name. "Not at all. On the contrary, people think it is a mountain, and walk right round it."

"I'm afraid I could never build anything so large as a mountain," said the Dottrel sadly.

"Don't you try," cried a Parrot cheerfully. "Don't you bother about building mounds or digging holes. You just look round for a nice comfortable hole in the top branch of the highest gum tree you can find, and you won't want anything better. That's the proper way to build a nest."

"But I would be frightened to live on the top branch of the highest gum tree," said the Dottrel, trembling at the thought.

"Well, that's the best advice I can give you," said the Parrot.

"Oh dear, oh dear!" said the Dottrel, "it is very perplexing. You all give me different advice, and each one tells me that his is the proper way of building a nest. Whom am I to believe?"

"Me! Me! Me!" cried each of the birds, shrieking and calling in such confusion that the poor little Dottrel was more bewildered than ever.

In the midst of it all a wailing voice whispered in his ear: "Take my advice. Don't build a nest at all, but put your eggs in the other birds' nests, and that will save you all trouble."

The Dottrel turned and faced the speaker indignantly.

"I know you, you are the Cuckoo," he said. "How dare you suggest anything so mean to me?" he exclaimed. "I may be young and stupid, but I'm not a sneak!"

The Cuckoo hunched his shoulders at the angry words, and skulked away without answering, leaving the Dottrel muttering to himself—"Put my eggs in other birds' nests, indeed! Not build a nest at all, indeed!"

"It's not a bad plan," said a Nightjar, a bird with big round eyes.

"What's not a bad plan?"

"To build no nest at all. I don't, and it saves a lot of trouble."

"But do you put your eggs in other birds' nests?" asked the Dottrel in surprise.

"Oh, no, I leave them on the ground in a sheltered spot and they are quite safe. Why, you could put your eggs on the sand, which they exactly resemble in colour, and no one would ever notice them."

"It would certainly save a lot of worry," said the Dottrel, "but isn't it a very lazy plan?"

"Of course it is," shrieked all the other birds. "You build a mud nest! No, a twig nest! No, a fibre nest! No, a bark nest! No, a reed nest!"

For a few moments the Dottrel was too bewildered to speak. Then suddenly he grew very angry, and pushing through them shouted loudly: "Stop your screaming and yelling! I don't want to know how any of your stupid old nests are made. I don't want a nest at all."

THE PROPER WAY

With these words he ran through their midst, and, scuttling over the ground as fast as his legs could carry him, disappeared through the grass at the edge of the lagoon.

And from that day to this he and his wife have never made a nest, but Mrs. Dottrel just leaves her eggs on the sand. And as they are of the same colour as the earth around them, they are as safe as they would be in any nest.

INQUISITIVE ROLEY

AMONGST the long cool grass at the edge of the pond lived Mrs. Frog and her family. There were five of them, all smooth and green and slippery, as frogs should be. They were Tippy, Slippy, Jumper, Hopper, and Roley—strange names, you may say, but just the proper ones for little frogs to have. There were all good children and lived very happily by the pond, spending their days in jumping about in the cool water, and their nights in singing on the brink. Five more contented little frogs it would have been hard to find.

Each day, their mother, who was a wise old frog, would teach them something new, so that they would be able to take care of themselves and keep from danger. She taught them how to hide among the reeds, and how to hop into the water if an enemy came near; and she warned them of the foes they must fear and avoid.

"Your two worst enemies," she said, "are little boys and snakes. Big men don't bother about us, as a rule, but little boys like to catch us and put us in bottles and tins, and there we very soon die, for there is no food."

"Do snakes put us in tins and boxes too?" asked Tippy.

"No, but they do worse things than that," said the mother gravely.

"What do they do?" asked all the froggies together in frightened voices.

"They eat us!" replied the mother, "but as long as you stay here you need not be afraid, for snakes won't chase you into the water. But you must never wander away by yourselves into the bush beyond."

"Oh no, we won't," cried the children, shivering and huddling up to each other.

And so they kept in the water, and would not venture beyond the very edge of the pond, for fear a snake should come out of the bush and seize them. At least, all of them except Roley. He was the youngest and should have been the most frightened of all, but instead of dreading the bush as the others did, he began to think of it in a way he had never done before. Until his mother had told him about the snakes, he had only noticed the bush as a place beyond the pond where the big trees grew, and had not thought much about it. But his mother's words had filled him with curiosity, and he spent nearly all his time wondering and wondering what the bush was like, and whether he could tell the difference beween a man and a little boy, and whether he would know a snake if he met one.

He could not ask his mother any questions, for when he mentioned the bush, his brothers all began to shiver so that his mother told him to be quiet and not talk about it.

So he asked a big old toad, who lived on the other side of the pond, what the bush was like, and if he could describe a snake to him.

"Don't ask me!" replied the toad in horror. "Don't talk to me about that awful bush, and those horrible, creeping, crawling snakes. Ugh!" and he shut his eyes with disgust and would not say another word.

Now instead of frightening Roley, this reply of the toad's only made him more inquisitive; so as no one would give him the information he wanted, his curiosity at last quite overcame his fear, and he decided to go off and find out for himself what the bush was like.

One thing he had learned from the old toad—that snakes were creeping, crawling things; but as he could hop farther and higher than any of his brothers, he did not think it would be hard for him to escape from a snake that could only creep and crawl. So one bright morning, when his mother had gone to see a friend a little way along the bank, and his brothers were all swimming about in the water, Roley slipped quietly through the reeds at the edge of the pond, and out into the clear grass beyond. For a few yards before him there was an open space, then came some small sheoaks, and behind them the bush.

It all looked so bright and sunny that Roley wondered that he could ever have been afraid of it. In the bush birds flew about singing gaily, and he could see bright flowers and green ferns beneath the trees. The ferns looked just as cool and safe as the reeds by the pond, so he thought he would hop across to them.

Just as he came out from the shelter of the reeds, and on to the open grass, he saw a huge figure coming towards him. He knew at once it was either a man

Roley hopped gaily forward

or a boy, and he stopped in doubt, for he did not want to be caught by a boy and put into a bottle. Then he remembered his mother had spoken of little boys and big men. Surely this creature was so monstrous that it must be a man, and his mother had said that big men did not catch frogs.

So thinking there was nothing to fear, he hopped gaily forward, right into the open space.

But it was a boy, and he instantly made a dart towards him, and Roley, thinking it was a game, hopped forward again. The boy made another dart, and almost caught him, but Roley hopped once more and gained the shelter of the ferns. There he sat and gazed round at the boy, who this time walked slowly towards him. Thinking the game was finished, Roley did not jump away, but sat still and watched the boy, who was soon quite close to him. Then, suddenly, before the frog could realize what was going to happen, the boy made a grab and caught him.

In vain he struggled and squirmed, he could not escape. The boy held him tightly in his hand for a few minutes, while Roley could hear him fumbling at something with his other hand. Next moment he was dropped into a box, the lid of which was immediately closed above him.

It was so dark in the box, that for a few minutes he could see nothing; then, as his eyes became accustomed to the dim light, he saw two bright eyes gazing at him, and could make out a strange form huddled up in one corner.

Roley's heart jumped with fear, but he was a brave little frog, and he would not show that he was afraid. So calling up all his courage, he raised his voice, and looking towards the strange figure, said politely—"Good morning."

At his words the bright eyes rose from the figure, and Roley could see that they were set in a small flat head on the end of a long neck. The head waved slowly from side to side, and a hissing voice said—"Good morning. I am very pleased to see you. I hope you are fat and well."

"Yes, thank you," replied Roley, "I am quite well."

"That's a good thing," said the other, "for you will make a nice juicy meal for me."

"I beg your pardon," stammered the frog, "but I don't want to be any kind of a meal."

The other laughed in a horrid jeering way, as he replied: "Then you shouldn't have come here."

"Who are you?" asked Roley.

"Who am I? I am the tiger snake, of course."

"The tiger snake!" echoed Roley, his voice trembling in spite of himself. "I didn't know that snakes lived in boxes."

"Neither they do," hissed the snake angrily, "and I don't mean to stay here very long. That boy has shut me up here, for he means to take me and show me off to his friends, but I don't intend to come back to this box."

"Why did he put me here? Is he going to show me off also?"

The snake laughed scornfully. "No," he said, "he is not going to show you off, but I am going to finish you off for my tea."

He hissed so horribly, and waved his head so excitedly that the frog jumped away into the farthest corner.

"Oh, I am not going to eat you yet," said the snake. "I have just had a good dinner." Then he curled himself round and went to sleep.

But poor Roley could not sleep. He was terrified, but in spite of his fear he did not lose his wits. When he was sure the snake was sound asleep, he hopped quietly round the box to see if there was any chance of getting out. But there were only three little holes to let in the air, and they were so small that he could scarcely get one foot into them. There was certainly no hope of escape there. Still he did not lose heart, but went back to his corner to think things over.

He remembered that the snake had boasted that the boy was going to show him to his friends. Now to do that he must open the lid of the box. Should he give a big jump directly the box was opened, and hop away? But the boy would see him, and perhaps chase him and catch him again. At last he determined to wait and see what opportunity there would be.

Just as he had come to this decision, the box was set down on the ground with a jerk which aroused the snake. He woke with a hiss, and turned to look at the frog.

"Ah, my little friend," he said, "you haven't much longer to live. The time has come now for me to be shown off. The boy thinks I will come back to this old box, but he is mistaken. Once I get out I mean to escape."

"I hope you will," said Roley.

The snake laughed sarcastically. "No doubt you do," he sneered, "but I don't mean you to escape. I shall take you with me."

At that moment the lid of the box opened; a long forked stick was poked in; and before the snake had time to know what was happening, he was lifted up and thrown out of the box.

90

INQUISITIVE ROLEY

Roley heard shrieks and screams as the snake disappeared from his sight, and he peeped over the edge of the box to see what was happening. He saw a lot of people standing round in a semi-circle, and on the grass before them lay the snake, his head lifted and waving furiously from side to side. Near him stood the boy who had caught Roley. In his hand he held a long forked stick, and every time the snake started to run across the grass, the boy would catch him behind the head with this stick, and bring him back. And every time he did so, the other people would laugh and clap their hands.

They were all so intent on the snake that they had no time to think of the frog. Roley saw this, and knew that now was his opportunity. Quietly he hopped out of the box, and with one leap, was across the grass and behind a bush. The snake saw him, and darted towards him, but before he could get half-way to the frog, the boy seized him with the stick and pinned him to the ground.

Roley waited to see no more, but started off with hops and leaps as fast as his legs could carry him, and at last he reached the pond.

Here he found his mother and brothers all very anxious about him, and when he told them of his adventures, the brothers trembled and shivered with fear.

His mother thought he had been sufficiently punished for his disobedience by the fright he had had, so she did not scold him. But when he had finished his story, she said: "I think you have all learned a lesson, my children. In future you will remember that—

Froggies are most safe at home,
Though larger animals may roam."

THE TALE OF TIBBIE

A LARGE sea anemone once lived in a shallow pool on the rocks of the Great Barrier Reef. She was a very big and beautiful anemone, quite unlike the pretty little ones you find round Sydney. She was as big as a large cabbage, and was of the most lovely sea-green colour. There were plenty of other pretty anemones around her, but she was the queen of them all. Her waving arms were soft like velvet, and glistened under the clear green water like fairyland flowers.

But though she was so beautiful, she was not at all vain and silly. In fact, she was just as sweet and kind as she was fair. She was very fond of all the small fishes and sea urchins who lived near her, and they all loved her. But the one she loved best was a dear little fish named Tibbie, and she was so fond of him that she let him live inside her. It may seem a funny place to live, but this anemone had such a big mouth that, when opened wide, it was almost like a room, and here little Tibbie lived very comfortably. He was a pretty little fish, about as big as a sardine, with a bright orange coat, pale yellow fins, and a nice clean white collar, of which he was extremely proud. He was a fish that anyone could have loved, and the anemone was very fond of him.

She did not even mind when he called her Annie, though her cousins teased her when they heard it, and one old anemone said:

"You shouldn't let that child be so familiar."

But Annie only laughed, and replied, "He is too little to say Anemone. And, besides, I like the name of Annie."

So Tibbie went on calling her Annie, and they were very happy together.

Sometimes he would stay out all day, playing with his friends, but he would always come back at night to his cosy little home. Annie used to worry when he stayed away all the day, for she was always afraid he might be eaten by a big fish. But Tibbie would only laugh and tell her not to worry, for he could swim as quickly as the big fish. So she did not bother him any more with her fears, but let him play and enjoy himself.

Never was there a happier little fish. All day long he would play with his little friends in the cool water. They had such fun together, playing hide-and-seek round the corals and seaweeds, or jumping up to try and catch the sunbeams as they flitted through the green water. Sometimes they would be very mischievous, and tease the sea urchins, who would try to spike them, but the little fishes were always too quick and managed to jump out of the way without being hurt. Sometimes they would be very quiet, and listen while Annie told them stories about the shark and the octopus, and the cruel big fish that ate the little fishes. The little creatures would all shiver with fright as they listened, still they enjoyed the stories very much.

The days passed by, each one very like another, and the little fishes played merrily and chased the small sea insects for their food; they lived in their pretty homes, and were just as happy as could be. Sometimes a big fish would come swimming by; then they would all rush to their homes, for most of them lived inside anemones, and, when there, they were quite safe, and could laugh at the big fish going by. But no big fish lived quite near, so as a rule they were left in peace.

One day, when they were all playing hide-and-seek round the coral, a Sea Urchin came hurrying towards them, looking very excited.

"Listen to me, listen to me!" he cried as he came near, and they all ran out of their hiding-places to hear what he had to say.

"What do you think has happened?" said the Sea Urchin, mysteriously.

"We don't know," said the little fishes, all shaking their heads.

"Guess!" said the Sea Urchin.

"You have a new spike," said one.

"No!"

"You've seen the shark," said another.

"No!"

"You've killed the octopus!" said a third.

"No!"

"You're a big silly," said Tibbie.

"No!" said the Sea Urchin; and all the little fishes laughed.

"Well, what?" they asked.

"A great Red Fish has come to live in the next pool!"

"Oh!" said the little fishes in horror.

"Yes; and, what is worse, he has brought his whole family with him!"

"O-o-oh!" wailed the little fishes. "O-o-oh, how dare he! How do you know?"

"I was sleeping quietly on the rocks, when I was suddenly wakened by a great swishing in the water. It seemed to come from the next pool, so I looked over the edge, and there I saw a great big fish in a beautiful black and red coat, and with him his wife and children. There must have been about twenty of them, and I nearly fell over among them. They didn't see me, so I sat quite still and listened. I heard the big fish say:

" 'This is a very nice pool, my dears. I think we'll stay here for a few weeks.' "

"Then his wife said: 'But is there anything about here to eat?' and the Red Fish replied: 'Oh, yes; there are plenty of little fishes among the anemones.' I didn't wait to hear any more, but came straight away to tell you."

When the Sea Urchin had finished speaking, the little fishes all looked sadly at each other. Then one said:

"Whatever shall we do?"

For a moment nobody answered, and then one very small fish said:

"Let us run home."

"What's the good of that?" said another. "We can't stay at home always. We must come out to get things to eat."

"Pooh!" cried Tibbie. "Who's frightened of the old fish? I'm not," and he puffed his chest out to look very big.

The other little fishes looked at him admiringly.

"Aren't you really frightened, Tibbie?" asked one.

"Of course I'm not," said Tibbie, boastingly. "Who cares for the Red Fish? They couldn't catch me. I think I'll go and have a look at them," he added, daringly.

The other little fishes stared in amazement, and thought him very brave, but none of them would venture to go with him. So they all swam away to their homes, whilst Tibbie started off to see the new arrivals.

At the edge of the pool was a thick fringe of sea-weed, and here Tibbie hid, for he did not want the Red Fish to see him. He peeped through the branches of the sea-weed, and there he saw a sight which, in spite of all his courage, made him very uneasy.

There were about twenty fishes in the pool, some much larger than others, but the very smallest was at least ten times as big as Tibbie. They had great wide mouths, and large hungry eyes, and they all looked as if they could easily eat a dozen little fishes for one meal.

94

THE TALE OF TIBBIE

Tibbie was really a brave little fellow, but he felt very frightened when he saw all these hungry monsters so close to him. He thought he would not wait to speak to them, and was just turning round to go back, when he heard a squeaking voice say, quite close to him:

"Oh, Ma, do come and look at this funny little fish."

Tibbie turned round quickly, for he did not like being called a "funny little fish," and, forgetting his fear and his grammar, said angrily:

"Who are you calling names?"

The Red Fish laughed rudely, and called out: "Oh, do come and look at him. He's angry now!"

In a moment Tibbie was surrounded by the school of Red Fish. He was too angry to be afraid, or to think of running away; so he stayed where he was without thinking of his danger.

"What's the matter with you?" asked one Red Fish.

"Nothing," said Tibbie, shortly.

"Have you got toothache?" asked another.

"No!" said Tibbie.

"Then why do you have your face tied up with a white handkerchief?" asked another. At this they all burst out laughing most rudely.

For a moment Tibbie did not know what they meant, and then suddenly he realized that they were laughing at his collar—his beautiful snowy white collar, of which he was so proud! He had never been so insulted in his life before, and he shouted at them:

"You are a set of dunces if you can't tell the difference between a collar and a handkerchief, and you're a lot of rude creatures."

The Red Fishes stared in astonishment, for they had not thought so small a fish would dare to answer them back in such a way. Then the mother Red Fish said angrily:

"You impudent sprat! I'll eat you up," and she made a rush at him. But before she could reach him, Tibbie had dived under the sea-weed, and was swimming as hard as he could for the other side. The Red Fish tried to follow him, but she was too big and was caught in the prickly branches.

When Tibbie had safely escaped from the Red Fish, he hurried home to tell Annie about the way he had been laughed at. He was very, very cross, and said:

"I'll punish them for laughing at me and my beautiful collar. Handkerchief, indeed! Toothache, indeed! I'll teach them the difference between a handkerchief and a collar!"

"But what can you do, dear?" said Annie. "You are too small to punish them."

"Oh, I'll do something. You wait till to-morrow," and he went off to bed.

He stayed awake a long time thinking and thinking of some way to punish the Red Fish, though when at last he fell asleep, he had not been able to form any plan that would do.

But the next morning he forgot all about the insult to his collar, for he had something more serious to think about.

When he went out to join his little friends as usual, he found only two, and they looked too white and frightened to play.

"What's the matter?" he asked. "Where are the others?"

"Oh, haven't you heard?" said one little fish.

"No," said Tibbie. "Heard what?"

"Early this morning, when our little friends came out to get their breakfasts, the whole family of Red Fish came rushing along and ate them all up."

"Oh, the cruel, cruel monsters!" cried Tibbie.

The two little fishes were weeping bitterly, as they said:

"All our playmates are gone, and the Red Fish will come and eat us next."

"Not if I know it," cried Tibbie, valiantly; "we must do something to punish them for that."

"We're too small to do anything," wept the two little fishes. "We're going home to hide from them."

"Don't be such cowards," cried Tibbie; but the two little fishes replied:

"We're not cowards, but we don't want to be dinners," and so saying they swam away, leaving Tibbie alone.

Tibbie did not notice that they had gone, for his whole mind was filled with thoughts of how to punish the wicked Red Fish for eating his little friends. He thought and thought, but could think of nothing that would do, and at last, in despair, he decided to go home and tell Annie all about it.

Anemone was very sad and sorry when she heard of the fate of the little fishes. She listened while Tibbie talked, and when he said angrily that he wished he was the shark, so that he could eat them up, she did not appear to hear him, for she was thinking hard. At last she said:

"How big did you say the Red Fish were, Tibbie?"

The red fish was almost touching his tail

"About ten times as big as me," Tibbie answered.

"Do you think they are fast swimmers?"

"I don't think they can swim very fast, indeed, for they couldn't catch me before I got into the shelter of the sea-weed."

Anemone didn't speak for a while; then she said:

"Are you nervous, Tibbie?"

"No," said Tibbie, indignantly; "you know very well I'm not."

"Would you be frightened to go to the Red Fishes' pool again?"

"No!" replied Tibbie.

"Then I have a plan to punish them which I think we can carry out. But first you must bring the Red Fish here one by one."

"How can I do that?" cried Tibbie.

"You must make them chase you, and you must swim straight to me as hard as you can, and they will follow you."

"But what will you do to them when they do come here?" asked Tibbie.

"Wait and you shall see," replied Anemone. "But the first thing for you to do is to bring them here."

"I'll soon do that," cried Tibbie, starting away at once.

"Remember, you bring only one at a time," Anemone called after him.

Now, that was not so easy. If he went straight up to the Red Fishes' pool and made them chase him, they would probably all come after him together, and that would not do. He must think this out. So he rested beneath the shelter of a coral branch to consider the matter.

He hadn't been there a minute when he saw a young Red Fish swimming along towards him. He was quite alone, and was looking for his dinner. As soon as he caught sight of Tibbie, he cried:

"Hullo, young toothache. Lend me your handkerchief."

"Booh," cried Tibbie. "You don't know a collar when you see it.

Dunce, dunce, double D,
Can't say your ABC."

"Oh, oh, you pert young sprat," said the Red Fish; "just wait a minute, and I'll have you for dinner."

He rushed towards Tibbie with his ugly mouth wide open. But Tibbie wasn't silly enough to wait for him. He darted out from the coral, calling as he went:

THE TALE OF TIBBIE

"Come on, dunce; come and catch me."

The Red Fish was furious, and came tearing after him as hard as he could. But Tibbie had a good start, and kept well ahead. They raced past the corals, the sea-weed, the starfish, and the sea urchins. Several anemones waved their arms to Tibbie to take shelter with them, for they all thought the Red Fish would catch him.

But Tibbie kept on and on, till at last he came in sight of his own dear Annie. She saw him coming, with the Red Fish giving chase, and waving her arms encouragingly, she called to him:

"Quickly, Tibbie; quickly."

The Red Fish heard her too, and, fearing that his prey was going to escape, he made a fresh effort, and almost caught up to Tibbie. The smaller fish heard his pursuer draw nearer, and for a moment he was afraid that he would be caught. He could see Anemone just ahead, but it seemed a long way to go with the Red Fish so close behind. If only she were a little nearer! He hoped her mouth would be wide open waiting for him. The Red Fish was almost touching his tail; in a few seconds he would be upon him.

"Annie, Annie!" he called. "Help me!"

Anemone opened her mouth wide; he made one last effort, and the next moment he was safe inside, just as the Red Fish reached him!

Then happened a strange thing. The Red Fish was swimming so hard that he could not stop himself, and he dived right into Anemone's mouth after Tibbie. Instantly, Anemone's arms closed round him, clutching him tight. In vain he struggled and squirmed. He was captured. Slowly Anemone clasped him tighter and tighter, and in a little while he was dead.

Tibbie looked on in silent awe, and when he saw that the Red Fish was killed, he asked Anemone:

"What are you going to do with him, Annie?"

"Eat him," replied Anemone. "I am very fond of fish, and they are my proper food, but I do not often get a chance to have one. The only way I can catch them is to grab them when they come chasing you."

And one by one nearly the whole of the Red Fishes chased Tibbie, and were caught and eaten by Anemone, until the remainder of the family, finding out what had happened became afraid of living so near the Anemone, and were even frightened to chase any little fishes at all. So they went away to deeper waters, and the little fishes were left in peace.

But you must not think that it was mere revenge that made the Anemone eat the Red Fish, for, unless she had big fish to eat sometimes, she could not live; nor, indeed, was it really cruelty that made the Red Fish eat the little fish, for they had also to feed on something, just as men eat sheep and cattle. And that is what wise men call "the survival of the fittest;" for it is one of the laws of Nature that the strongest shall always devour the weakest. Still, it is very hard for the little fish, isn't it? I don't wonder that Tibbie rebelled against such a law. Do you?

THE BIRDS' ALPHABET

THE Australian birds were having a meeting to consider what they could do to become better friends with the Humans.

All the birds of the land were gathered together, and even the birds from the sea. It wasn't very comfortable for the sea birds, as they were not used to sitting on trees, and the Albatross could not balance himself, but kept falling from side to side, till a Cocktail asked him if he should bring him a bucket of water to sit in. This made all the birds laugh so much that at last the Emu had to call for order, and then the meeting began.

"The first thing to do," said the Pelican, "is to bring ourselves into notice."

"You wouldn't have much trouble to do that," sneered the Kookaburra, at which all the little birds tittered, for the Pelican's beak is very long and big.

But they didn't laugh long, for the Pelican opened his mouth wide, and said angrily: "If you small fry don't keep quiet, I'll swallow you all."

"Order, order!" said the Emu. "We must not begin with a quarrel."

"Well, you make that old jackass keep his nonsense to himself," growled the Pelican.

"As the Pelican has already remarked," said the Emu, "the first thing to do is to bring ourselves into notice. Now how are we to do it?"

"Have our portraits taken," said the Native Companion, who knew she was handsome.

"Oh, but that wouldn't teach them our names," said the Albatross, who knew that he never looked his best in a photograph.

"Let us have a procession through the streets," said a Blue Crane, who was an elegant walker.

"Oh, yes, and get snared and put into cages," objected the Parrot, and all the other small birds agreed with him.

"No, I don't think any of those ways would do," said the Emu. "We must make them hear of us in some way."

"I know," suddenly called out a small, brown bird in a clear, sweet voice. "Let us sing songs about ourselves."

It was the Reed-Warbler who spoke, and he was noted for his good singing.

Several of the birds called out, "That's a good plan. We agree to that. Let us sing songs about ourselves," and then they all shouted, "Agreed, agreed."

"Very fine," said the Kookaburra, who was in a very bad temper, "but where are you going to get the songs?"

The birds all looked at each other in dismay. They hadn't thought of that. It was easy enough to sing songs if you had them, but there were no songs written about them, although there were plenty about English skylarks and cuckoos.

"Well, we must have some written," said the Emu at last.

"Who will write them?" asked the Parrot.

That was a difficult question, and again they all looked at each other. No one had an answer ready, and it seemed as if there would be no songs written. The Kookaburra began to laugh scornfully, and said in a jeering way, "Your plan does not seem to have much chance, Mister Emu."

But suddenly a little, olive-green bird flew down in the centre of the group, and said in a sweet voice, "Please, Mister Emu, I have a suggestion to make."

"Very well, Silvereye," said the Emu, "let us have it."

The little bird drew himself up with an important air, and said, "I propose that we all make up songs about ourselves. Let us begin with the letter A, and go through the alphabet, and every bird must sing a song when it comes to his initial."

"That is an excellent plan," said the Emu. "I think we'll adopt it."

"Agreed, agreed," cried the birds, whilst the Silvereye modestly retired to the background to his friends the little Tits and Tomtits.

"How did you think of such a good idea, Sivie?" asked the little Tits.

The Silvereye looked round to see that no one was listening, and then he whispered quietly, "I knew there was no one whose name began with Z except me!"

"But yours doesn't," said a Tomtit, "Silvereye begins with S."

"Yes, but my real name is 'Zosterops,' and that begins with Z."

"Oh, what a name!" cried the little Tits. "Where did you get it?"

"The man at the Museum calls me that, so it must be right, and there are no other Z's."

"You're rather cunning, Sivie," said the little Tits.

"Silence! you youngsters," called the Emu. "We are going to begin." Then he cleared his throat, and said in a loud voice, "As A is the first letter we had better begin with that. Let me see, what does A stand for?"

"A stands for Albatross," shrieked the sea birds in chorus.

"Then let the Albatross come here into the centre of the circle and sing about himself," said the Emu.

The Albatross made an effort to get off the branch where he was sitting, but he is always a slow bird at starting, though he goes like the wind when he is flying.

Before he could reach the ground, a long-legged bird with a long turned-up bill walked into the centre.

"A is for Avocet," he said grandly.

"A is for 'Ave-a-nose, I should think," said a little Tit, and all the little birds began to giggle.

"Order!" cried the Emu, while the Avocet looked round indignantly.

"Go on, Avocet," said the Emu. "As you begin with A, and the Albatross is so slow, you must make your song."

"A is for Avocet
With a beautiful nose,"

began the long-legged bird, but he was interrupted by the Kookaburra, who called out in a loud voice—

"It's trying to get
To the sky I suppose."

He then burst out laughing, while some of the other birds laughed too, for the Avocet's nose is quite different from any other bird's in being turned up at the end.

"Order!" called the Emu, "let the Avocet finish his song."

But the Avocet was too angry, and stalked proudly away.

"Well, let us go on to the next," said the Emu. "What does B stand for?"

"Blue-wren," said a small, long-tailed blue and black bird as he hopped into the centre.

"Bower Bird," said a beautiful, sheeny-blue bird, running in front of the Emu.

"Yes, I think it must be for Bower Bird," said the Emu, and the small bird with the long tail retired with a downcast air.

The Bower Bird flew backwards and forwards as he sang—

"B is for Bower Bird,
Happy and gay.
He builds a fine bower
In which he can play."

"Very good, very good," called the birds as they applauded.

"C comes next," said the Emu. "What does C stand for?"

"Cocktail," said the little bird with the long tail, as he again hopped into the centre.

"No, C is for Cockatoo," shrieked a big, white bird with a yellow crest, as he flew down.

The small bird looked at him for a moment, then, as the big bird was more than twenty times his size, he hopped away quickly, looking very disappointed.

"Never mind," said the kind-hearted Jacky Winter to him, "your turn will come later on."

The Cockatoo had a very loud voice, and he began his song in a shriek that nearly deafened the others—

"C is for Cockatoo
With a fine crest of yellow."

"Who makes us all deaf
With his horrible bellow,"

interrupted the Kookaburra quickly.

The Cockatoo was so surprised that he just shrieked, and flew back to his place.

"I think we had better have another song for C," said the Emu, "for no one will want to sing that. Won't you make a song, Curlew?"

"A tall, sad bird walked slowly into the centre, and began in a mournful voice—

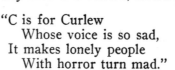

"C is for Curlew
Whose voice is so sad,
It makes lonely people
With horror turn mad."

"Oh-oh, he gives me the shudders," said a Jacky Winter, "I do hate those sad songs. I wish they had let you sing your song, Cocktail, instead."

"I'm sure it would have been brighter than that," said the Cocktail.

"D," called the Emu. "Who stands for D?"

A tiny, spotted bird crept into the centre, and said in a squeaky voice, "I am a Diamond Bird; will I do?"

"You're very small," said the Emu, stooping down to look at her.

"It's time a small bird sang," called out a little Tit, "all the others have been big fellows."

"Very well," said the Emu, "you may sing." So the little bird sang in a tiny voice—

"D is for Diamond Bird
Fluffy and round,
I lay my white eggs
In a hole in the ground."

"That's a very pretty little song," said the Emu, when she had finished, and the little bird crept shyly away.

"She's silly to tell where she makes her nest," said a Tomtit. "How does she know the Cuckoo is not listening?"

"E comes next," called the Emu. "What does E stand for?"

"Emu, of course," said the Kookaburra scornfully. "Won't you make a pretty song about yourself, Mister Chairman?"

The Emu looked rather annoyed and uncomfortable, but before he could answer the Kookaburra, the Parrot shouted: "Yes, E is for Emu," and then all the birds sang in chorus—

"E is for Emu
Stately and grand,
He is the emblem
Of our native land."

When they had finished, the Emu looked very pleased as he said: "Thank you very much. You are all very kind. Let us go on to F."

"F is for Flycatcher," said several birds together, and they all flew down to the centre and stood in a row. There were Jacky Winter, Willy Wagtail, two Miss Fantails, the Razor Grinder, and several others.

"Which of you will make the song?" asked the Emu, for several of them were good singers.

"All of us," they replied, and together they sang—

"Flycatchers all are we,
Happy as birds can be.
In an elegant way
Our tails we display
As anyone here can see."

Here they all wagged their tails from side to side, and went on to the second verse—

> "Insects and flies we eat,
> Thinking them nice and sweet;
> We dart on the wing
> And snap up each thing
> That's likely to give us a treat."

The other birds here burst out in loud applause, and the Flycatchers all bowed, wagged their tails, and flew back to their places.

"That was really a very fine song," said the Emu.

"Very vain song," sneered the Kookaburra. "I should like to know why they are so proud of their tails. They are very ordinary tails."

"I think you would be proud if you had one half as good," said the Parrot, and the other birds laughed, for the Kookaburra has a very small tail for his size.

"G comes next," said the Emu, "who stands for G?"

"We do," said the Gulls and Gannets, all flying down in a flock.

"Well, which of you is going to sing?" asked the Emu.

"The Gulls," said the Gannets.

"No, the Gannets," said the Gulls.

"This won't do," reproved the Emu. "One of you must sing the song."

"The Gannet began it," called out a little Tit, which of course made all the other Tits giggle.

"Well, the Gulls must finish if we begun it," said a Gannet.

"But we can't sing," squawked the Gulls.

"Neither can we," squawked the Gannets.

"This is awkward," said the Emu, looking worried, but before he had time to say another word the Kookaburra shouted: "As the Gulls and Gannets can't sing a song for themselves, I'll make one for them—

> "The Gannet and Gull
> Are too thick in the skull
> To make up a rhyme;
> And so to save time
> I'll sing one myself."

"Pooh!" shouted the little birds, "do you call that poetry?"

The Emu looked very grave as he said sternly to the Kookaburra, "It's not only very bad poetry, but it's very bad manners." At which the Kookaburra burst out laughing.

"We haven't yet had a song for G. Isn't there any other G?" asked the Emu.

A funny little grey bird with a sleek, round body and short legs waddled into the centre. It was the Grebe, whom some people call the Dabchick.

"I'm a G," he said.

"Very well, you sing a song," said the Emu.

The little bird stood alone in front of the chairman, and, lifting up his little head, made a very funny little noise, just like a nannygoat. He kept this up for several minutes, till even the most sedate birds were laughing, and the little birds were nearly bursting.

"He must be a G," shrieked a little Tit, "for G stands for Goat."

The little bird took no notice, but went on with his funny noise, till at last the Emu had to say: Thank you, I think you have sung enough."

The little bird bobbed his head and waddled away.

"Still we have no song for G," said the Emu.

"I'll make one," said a little brown bird shyly. "I'm the Grass-bird," and he began to sing in a quiet voice—

> "G is for Grass-bird,
>   Too shy to speak,
>   He whistles all night
>   In the reeds of the creek."

"Ah, that's better," said the Emu. "And now let us go on to the next, for we really must not spend so much time on one letter. Who stands for H?"

A lot of birds of different sizes and colours flew down. Some were brown, some green, some black and yellow, but they all had the same kind of long sharp beak. They stood round in a circle and began all together—

> "H is for Honeyeater—"

Here they were interrupted by the Kookaburra, who gave a loud laugh and said—

> "H is for Honeyeater,
>   Of which there are dozens,
>   Fathers and brothers,
>   And uncles and cousins."

The Honeyeaters were too angry and insulted to go on with their song, so they all flew back to their places, poking out their long feathery tongues at the Kookaburra as they passed.

"Kookaburra," said the Emu sternly, "if you cannot behave better, you will have to leave the meeting." Then, pointedly turning his back to the interrupter, he asked, "Who will sing next?"

"I," said a white bird with a long curved beak which almost reached the ground. He walked slowly up to the Emu in a very grave manner and said: "I is for Ibis. I am the Ibis."

"Oh, yes," said the Emu, "of course I know you. Will you sing a song about yourself?"

"I can't sing," said the grey bird gravely.

"Then who is to make a song about you?" asked the Emu.

"Any one who likes."

The Emu looked round with a puzzled air, fearing that the Kookaburra would come in with something rude, but before he had a chance, a little Tit jumped up and said: "I know one about him—

> "I is for Ibis
>   Whose nose is so long
> You really can't put him
>   In such a small song."

The Emu was afraid that the Ibis would be offended at this, but he just turned and looked at the little Tit gravely, and, shaking his head sadly, said: "That's quite true. That will do." Then he walked wearily away.

"Now for J," said the Emu.

Immediately all the birds shouted together—

> "J is for Jackass
>   That silly old fowl,
> Who giggles and laughs
>   With a horrible howl.
>
> "He says silly things
>   And thinks himself clever,
> But a more stupid bird
>   You couldn't find ever."

As they sang they all pointed at the Kooka-burra, who shook with rage on his branch.

"How dare you call me a Jackass?" he shouted. "You know my name is Kookaburra."

"They call you a Jackass because you are so stupid," said the Emu, "and I must say you have brought it on yourself. Now let us go on to K."

"K is for Kookaburra," cried the Kookaburra quickly, but all the others called out: "Oh, no, your song has been sung, and you cannot have another. K is for Kestrel."

"Yes, K is for me," said the Kestrel, looking so fierce that the Kookaburra was afraid to say another word, but sulked on his branch.

> "K is for Kestrel
> A fierce bird of prey,
> But don't be alarmed,
> He's quite gentle to-day."

sang the Kestrel, while the little birds edged away from him in a frightened manner.

"I think L comes next," said the Lyre Bird, dancing in the ring, "and of course that stands for me."

"Oh, yes, will you give us a song?" asked the Emu.

"With pleasure." And with a stately bow the Lyre Bird began to sing—

> "The Lyre Bird is a singer fine,
> So listen to my song,
> And as I haven't much to say,
> It will not keep you long.
>
> "I mimic every bird that sings,
> Though he be large or small,
> No bird's song is too hard for me,
> But I can mimic all."

"That's very true," said the Emu, when the Lyre Bird had waltzed out of the circle. "Now for M."

"M is for Morepork," said several birds, "where is he?"

"There he is, asleep as usual," cried a little Tit. "Wake him up and make him sing."

It was hard to find the Morepork, for he was sitting on a branch of a stringy bark, and his feathers were so exactly the colour of the tree that it was hard to see which was the branch and which was the bird. But the Parrot saw him and gave him a poke with his beak, saying, "Get up and sing a song."

The Morepork stirred uneasily, and said in a grumbling voice: "Leave me alone, I want to sleep. I didn't get a wink last night."

"I am afraid you are getting into very bad habits, Morepork," said the Emu gravely. "Why don't you go to bed at sunset like all well-behaved birds?" Then as the Morepork only grunted and settled himself down to go to sleep again, the Emu said: "We must have someone else for M, for we'll never waken him."

"We'll sing for you," called two birds together, as they flew down to the singing place, "we are Martins." They were both grey-blue birds and very much alike, but one had a black face and the other had white eyebrows. They were such pretty, graceful birds that it didn't seem to matter that their voices were not very pleasant as they sang—

"M is for Martin;
    Cousins are we,
And each of us builds
    In the fork of a tree.

"We travel together,
    And build near each other,
For we are as friendly
    As brother and brother."

"Now that is the kind of song I like to hear," said the Emu, as the two Martins flew away. "Let us see if we cannot have more in the same strain. Who stands for N?"

"I do," said the Native Companion, as she walked gracefully into the centre. She was a beautiful bird with lovely, grey feathers and a long graceful neck, and as the other birds looked at her they wondered that no Australian poet had sung about her. Before saying anything she spread out her wings and danced a few steps of the minuet, then began to recite—

"N is for Native Companion so tall,
Wherever I dance I'm the belle of the ball,
On the far western plains of the country I live,
By my beauty and grace much pleasure I give."

As she spoke she danced backwards and forwards in so pretty a fashion that none of the other birds noticed the vanity of her words except the Kookaburra. He had been silent and sulky since they had all made fun of him, but now he burst out with a loud laugh.

"Is that the tone of song you like, Mister Emu? So modest and simple. Let me add another verse," and before anyone could stop him, he shouted—

"N is for Native Companion so vain,
A long-legged lanky, decidedly plain."

"Shame, shame!" cried the birds in chorus while the poor Native Companion

110

looked miserable, for she was not really vain, but only pleased that she could dance gracefully.

"Take no notice of him," said the Emu scornfully, "let us go on to O. Where is O?"

"Here," said a long-legged bird with a long beak. Without wasting time, he began to say in a quick voice—

> "O is for Oyster-catcher
> (What a horrible name!)
> The crabs and fish avoid me,
> But I catch them just the same."

"Very good!" shouted the sea birds, "that's an interesting song."

"Yes, it's very nice," said the Emu politely, though really he wasn't much interested in crabs and fish. "Now who stands for P?"

A queer-looking black and white bird waddled into the centre. He had feet like a duck, and instead of wings he had two funny little skinny flappers. As soon as he appeared the Kookaburra burst out laughing, and called out—

> "P is for Penguin,
> A funny old chap;
> His two little wings
> Can do nothing but flap."

Then to everyone's surprise, the Penguin turned towards the Kookaburra and said: "Thank you very much. That's just what I would have said myself, only I couldn't have put it so nicely." Then he waddled gravely away.

The Kookaburra was too astonished to reply, for he certainly had not meant to be nice, and he felt very silly at the Penguin's words.

"Q comes next. What does Q stand for?"

"Quail," called a little brown bird, as he came running up, and he sang in a sad voice—

> "Q is for Quail,
> Whose home's on the ground;
> He runs through the grass,
> And makes not a sound.

> "But when sportsmen come
> With dog and with gun,
> The poor little Quail
> Finds it's no good to run."

"Poor little chap," said the Emu kindly, "You do have a bad time indeed. Now what does R stand for?"

"I'll sing for R," said a dark-blue bird about the size of a fowl. He had a bright red beak, and long, red legs, and as he walked into the centre he pointed his toes and whisked up his tail to show the white feathers beneath it. He was such a handsome bird, that if he did seem rather conceited there was some excuse for him. He had a queer voice, but he began to sing—

> "R is for Red-bill,
>   My home is so damp,
> I expect you all wonder
>   I don't get the cramp.
>
> "But water and mud
>   Are the best things for me,
> And I should feel awkward
>   Perched up in a tree."

Then he flicked up his tail and stalked away.

"Who will sing a song for S?" asked the Emu.

An odd little bird with a little body on very long legs walked up.

"I'm a Stilt," he said, "I'll sing for S." And he sang—

> "S is for Stilt,
>   Who lives in the reeds,
> His long legs are useful
>   To wade through the weeds."

"T's next," cried the Emu. "Who stands for T?"

"I do. I do. I do. I do," called the Tom-tits, Tree-creepers, Thrushes, and Thickheads all together.

"Dear me!" said the Emu, "do you all begin with T? But you can't all sing, you know. Which of you will make a song?"

"None of them," cried a harsh voice. "The land birds have sung too much. I'm a Tern, and I'm going to sing now, for it's time the sea birds had a turn."

"But they always have a Tern," cried a little Tit, who hadn't a chance to show his wit for some time.

"I think you're trying to make a joke," said the Tern, "but at any rate I'm going to have a turn now," and he sang in a wild, harsh voice—

> "T is for Tern
>   Who skims o'er the sea,
> And gracefully dives
>   In the waves for his tea."

"That's very nice," said the Albatross, "but it makes me feel hungry."

"Yes, it must be nearly time for tea," agreed the Emu. "We must hurry through the rest. Who is for U?"

There was no answer. The birds looked at each other in silence, and thought of each other's names, but no one knew of a U.

"Ha, ha, ha!" suddenly laughed the Kookaburra, "I'm the only U amongst you."

"But you're K," said the Emu.

"No, J," called the little Tits.

"No, I'm U," shrieked the Kookaburra. "U stands for useful, and I'm the only useful one among you, for I kill snakes!"

"Well, if no one's name begins with U, let us go on to V. Who stands for V?"

Again there was silence, and again all the birds looked at each other. The Emu was just going to say, "Go on to W," when a small bird hopped shyly up. It was a cousin to the Blue-wren, and very much like him, but it had brown patches on its shoulders, and it was much shyer than the Blue-wren. It spoke in a whisper, as if frightened of being heard, and said: "In some books I'm called the Variegated Wren. Will that do for V?"

"What a name!" said a little Tit; "no wonder he whispers it."

"Yes, that will do for V," said the Emu. "Can you sing a song about yourself?"

"V is for Variegated," began the little bird, then looked round in a frightened way, and saying, "I can't find a rhyme for that," hopped quickly away.

"It is a difficult word," said the Emu. "We won't try to find a rhyme. Let us go on to W."

"W is for Wonga," cried a big blue Pigeon, who began to sing in a plaintive voice—

> "W's for Wonga
> Who's so good to eat
> That sportsmen will chase him
> Into his retreat."

"Now for the next letter," cried the Emu. "X comes next. But who stands for X?"

"The Jackass," called a little Tit, "because he's extra silly."

"I'm afraid we'll have to leave X," said the Emu, "and go on to Y."

"I'm the only Y," said the Yellowbob. "I know I'm really a Robin, but as the Robins didn't sing, don't you think I may sing for Y?"

"Yes, I think so," said the Emu, and the Yellowbob began to sing—

"Y is for Yellowbob,
Friendly am I,
I do not fear men,
And so I'm not shy."

"That's a dear little song," said the Emu. And now there's only one letter left. What does Z stand for?"

"Me!" shrieked the Silvereye, so excitedly that he could hardly get it out.

"You?" said the Emu in surprise. "Oh, I think you've made a mistake. Silvereye begins with S."

"Yes, but my proper name is Zosterops," cried the Silvereye, proudly.

"Zoster-what?" exclaimed the Emu. "Whoever told you that?"

"The man at the Museum calls me Zosterops," said the Silvereye grandly.

"Well he ought to know," said the Emu. "Can you sing a song about it?"

"Z is for Zosterops,"

began the Silvereye, then stopped to think. "Z is for Zosterops," he began again, and again stopped. Then before he could make a third attempt the Kookaburra called out—

"Z is for Zosterops,
Oh, what a name!
No wonder the Silvereye
Stutters with shame."

At this all the little birds giggled, for they thought it great fun that the Silvereye could not make a song about himself, when he had been the one to suggest it.

"Never mind, Silvereye," said the Emu kindly, "perhaps you'll be able to finish it another time. And now, as we have gone through the alphabet, I think we should sing a chorus to conclude." Then they all sang and their united song was so beautiful that Humans stopped in their work to listen, and admire. So the birds got the attention that they wanted, and ever since they and the Humans have been the best of friends.

114